Contents

CHAPTER ONE: THE HEALTH DEBATE ....

- Health of the Nation
- Delivery of Health Care Services
- Dilemmas in Health Care

CHAPTER TWO: THE FIRST THIRTY YEARS 8

- Health Services Before 1948
- The Founding Principles of the National Health Service
- Medical Advances
- Finance
- Structural Change

CHAPTER THREE: THE NHS UNDER THE CONSERVATIVES 16

- The 1982 Reorganisation
- Search for Better Management
- Privatisation
- Developments in Primary Care
- Health Promotion
- Community Care
- The Patient's Charter

CHAPTER FOUR: SETTING OUT THE NHS MARKET 27

- Crisis in the NHS
- The New NHS
- The New Structure
- The New NHS: Surgery or Butchery?
- The Purchaser–Provider Split
- Fundholding GPs
- Self-Governing Trusts

CHAPTER FIVE: GOING PRIVATE 38

- The Tradition of Private Health Care
- Support for Privatisation
- Private Health Insurance
- Private Hospitals
- Public–Private Partnerships
- Competitive Tendering
- Privatisation and Primary Care
- Privatisation and the Future

CHAPTER SIX: INEQUALITIES IN HEALTH 51

- Health and Illness
- Geographical Inequalities
- Social Class Inequalities
- Gender Inequalities
- Ethnic Inequalities

CHAPTER SEVEN: THE ELDERLY—A CASE STUDY 66

- An Ageing Population
- The Health of the Elderly
- Health Services for the Elderly
- Care in the Community

CHAPTER EIGHT: THE POLITICAL ARENA 81

- Employees
- Voice of the Public
- Commercial Interests
- Political Parties

CHAPTER NINE: BACK TO THE FUTURE 89

- An Assessment of the NHS
- The Future of Health Care
- Quality Adjusted Life Years

Chapter ONE
The Health Debate

PICK UP a newspaper almost any day of the week and you will find yourself reading headlines such as these. Switch on a television or radio and it is likely that you will be able to watch or listen to programmes dealing with many issues relating to our health. Visit any bookshop or library and you will be confronted with row after row of titles devoted to health care. Visit any newsagent's and you will see a wide range, and growing number, of specialist magazines which tell us how to adopt a more healthy lifestyle.

Clearly the health of our nation and the state of our health care services are matters of tremendous public interest. Moreover, since they are concerned with issues of life and death, this means that they are inevitably emotive subjects, provoking strong views and a great deal of controversy.

HEALTH OF THE NATION

Optimistic View

On the face of it, there does not appear to be grounds for debate over the general health of the population. Since the beginning of the nineteenth century there has been a steady and, at times, dramatic improvement in the country's health. At that time, life expectancy was low and the infant mortality rate—the number of children dying within a year of their birth—was high. Terror diseases such as cholera, typhoid and smallpox swept through whole communities decimating their populations. By the end of the nineteenth century, however, medical advances and, more importantly, public health reforms, better housing conditions and improvements in the production and distribution of food had greatly reduced the infant mortality rate and enabled people to live longer and healthier lives. We have been able to spend more money on medical care and research in the last twenty years than we spent throughout the whole of our history on earth. In the 1990s, our hospitals are equipped with much high-technolgy machinery which allows doctors to perform miracles of science such as organ transplants and also to produce what the media proclaim as new 'wonder' drugs. We now have more people than ever before in this country who survive well into their seventies, eighties and nineties. It is little wonder that many people are confident that modern medicine is now on the verge of conquering the majority of killing and disabling diseases.

Pessimistic View

To others, however, this optimism is completely unfounded. Indeed, in some respects, they claim we are sicker than our ancestors, not healthier. While we may have all but beaten many of the old killer diseases, we have only managed to replace them with the so-called major epidemics of the 20th century—heart disease, strokes, high blood pressure, obesity, cancer, stress-related disorders and new social diseases such as Acquired Immune Deficiency Syndrome (AIDS). More people are now living into old age, but this has been accompanied by an increase in the mortality rate for young men and women in their thirties and their forties. Farmers and food manufacturers may have ensured that we now have more food to eat, but

recent media reports, such as the controversies over the issues of irradiated food and diseases such as Bovine Spongiform Encephalopathy (BSE), or 'Mad Cow Disease' as it has become known, have raised questions about the safeness of our diet. Scientists and the drug industry have developed many useful new medical treatments, but they have been accused of sloppy techniques at the trial stages. These have allowed some products with dangerous side effects onto the market, the Thalidomide tragedy of the 1960s being a dramatic but by no means isolated case. Doctors have been accused of over-prescribing inappropriate and highly addictive tranquilliser drugs such as Valium and Librium instead of spending a little more time talking and listening to their patients. It is claimed that our hospitals have been more interested in acquiring expensive high-technology machinery than in diverting their resources into the less glamorous but more essential areas such as treatment of the elderly, the mentally handicapped and the disabled.

DELIVERY OF HEALTH CARE SERVICES

The delivery of our health care services has also been moved to the centre of the national stage. Ever since its introduction in 1948, the sheer size of Britain's National Health Service (NHS), in terms of both personnel and finance, has made it an inevitable candidate for political and public debate. In 1994, for example, the NHS provided employment for over one million people from a variety of professions, making it the largest single employer in Europe. It consumes more than one-fifth of all spending, thus being a more costly programme for the government than defence or education. What has emerged recently, however, is a new ferocity in this political debate.

The consensus which existed between the political parties that, along with the monarchy, the NHS was one of the two unassailable institutions on the British political scene, seems to have been well and truly shattered.

Positive View

On the one side are those who view the NHS as the most essential and praiseworthy of all our institutions. When it came into existence it broke completely new ground in the Western world. It was the first health system to offer free medical care on demand at the point of use to the whole population. It was also the first fully comprehensive system to be based on the state provision of medical care rather than of the insurance principle which enabled only those who had made contributions to receive treatment. Thus, the free, comprehensive and universal nature of the NHS made it a unique example in the collective provision of health care. Over the years it has, it is claimed, made a significant contribution to the continuing improvement of the nation's health and of all our institutions it is the one which is viewed with most envy by people throughout the world. The NHS may well have its faults but this, it is argued, is due more to issues of underfunding and administrative weakness than to any basic problem in how the service is delivered or to its founding principles.

Negative View

Nevertheless, the NHS has also had its fair share of critics. Ever since its creation, the NHS has been attacked for being a sickness-orientated rather than a health-orientated service. It is too concerned, the argument goes, with the treatment of those who have already lost their health and pays too little attention to preventing people losing their health in the first place. More recently, it has been severely criticised for being both costly and inefficient. It is claimed that this dissatisfaction with the NHS has been clearly illustrated by the increased popularity in the last few years of both alternative, or complementary, medicine and private medicine.

With regard to cost, it is a fact that over the years, many groups have constantly, and successfully, demanded that more resources be pumped into the NHS. In 1948 it soaked up 4.2% of our Gross National Product (GNP) while in 1993 this had

risen to 6%. In 1993–94 public expenditure on the NHS exceeded £35 billion, with the private sector consuming another £1.5 billion. Despite this, it is widely perceived that the reason why the health of the nation continues to be an issue of public concern is that the NHS is seriously underfunded. Its critics, however, claim that no matter how much money is thrown at the NHS, the country's health problems will never be properly tackled until there is a complete re-examination of priorities within the system. For example, instead of wasting huge amounts of money on high-technology medicine or on constantly searching for mythical wonder cures, both of which can benefit only a few people, the NHS should divert its resources towards ensuring that the majority of its clients can enjoy a much higher basic level of care.

The most glaring indicator of the inefficiency and incompetence of the NHS is our enormous national hospital waiting list. Throughout the 1980s the official number of patients on waiting lists remained in the range of between 600,000 and 800,000. In 1993, Health Department figures showed hospital waiting lists above the million mark for the first time since records began. Many people have claimed, however, that the official statistics exclude patients who are in need of treatment but who have not referred themselves, and so the real number of people waiting is even higher. Indeed, a number of those who are waiting to be admitted to hospital are classified as non-urgent, and so although many of these may be painful cases, a large number of them have to wait on the list for a year or more.

The main problem though, is that while we have a so-called *National* Health Service, the length of time that a patient has to wait for consultations and operations, and also the quality of a person's general standard of health, depends to a large extent on which part of the country he or she happens to live in or to which social class he or she belongs.

DILEMMAS IN HEALTH CARE

There may well be disagreement over the state of the nation's health and over the delivery of the health care services, but there is no argument over the fact that modern medicine is in a constant state of change. While developments in medical technology and new branches of science such as molecular biology have opened up promising opportunities for improving the treatment of a substantial number of patients, they have also at the same time, presented us with a number of uncomfortable moral, legal, social and economic dilemmas.

New 'breakthroughs' in medical technologies such as computer tomography (CT scanners) and magnetic resonance imaging (MRI), both of which are used for diagnosing patients, and also the use of lasers in surgery, offer patients safer, less painful and more effective care than that provided by previous procedures. The problem with many of these high-technology developments, however, is that they are very expensive. For example, each MRI facility costs nearly £1 million to buy and about £250,000 a year to run. This has meant that the availability and use of many technologies, even so-called 'essential' life-saving technologies, have been restricted. This, in turn, has raised questions on how we should ration health care. Since there are not enough kidney dialysis machines to meet the large demand for them, for example, how should we go about deciding who has access to them? The dilemmas involved in the adoption of new medical technologies can be best illustrated by looking at the right to life and the right to die, two debates which have received a tremendous amount of media attention in recent times.

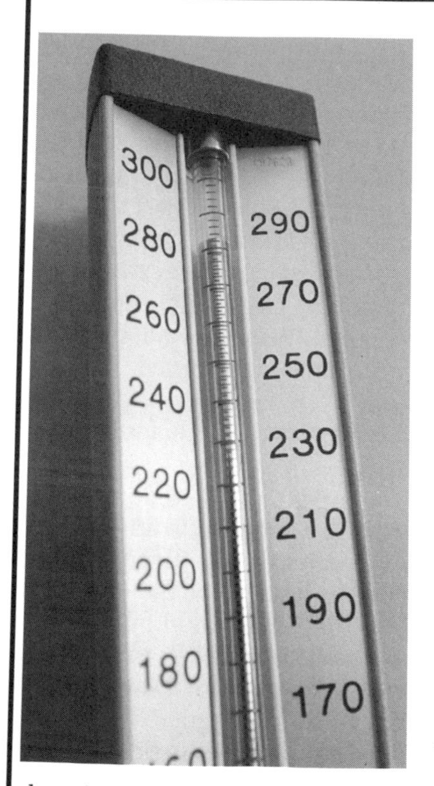

The Right to Life?

THIS DEBATE has focused on new technologies used to treat infertile women. When the world's first test-tube baby was born in 1978, there was widespread alarm concerning how such children would come to terms with having two mothers. Society, generally, has come to accept this practice but, more recently, the suggestion that eggs from aborted foetuses could be transplanted into infertile women has reopened the whole issue. On the one hand, this latest proposal is seen by many as a possible new important source of donor eggs, which are in short supply at the moment, to help the involuntary childless. On the other hand, fears have been expressed about people playing God or Frankenstein, using spare parts from unborn children for the artificial creation of life, and about the effect on children born in such circumstances to cope with the fact that their biological mother had never been born.

The Right to Die?

AT THE other end of the life span, high-technology medicine has the ability to keep the body biologically alive beyond the time when the patient can make a recovery. While the prolonging of life may be seen as a worthy objective, it does raise a number of controversial issues. Are the costs of keeping patients artificially alive justified? Are these technologies used appropriately or are they merely inflicting unnecessary suffering? Do the terminally ill and those suffering from intolerable illness have the right to decide on euthanasia? Who, if anyone, should be permitted to decide whether to withhold life-sustaining treatment? Should heart or brain death determine when an organ can be taken away from a patient for transplantation purposes?

These and many other dilemmas have arisen due to the great advances which have occurred in medicine in recent years. In order to understand the present and developments which may take place in the future, however, it is first of all necessary to take a brief look at the past. This is done in the following chapter.

Chapter TWO
The First Thirty Years

BEFORE examining the period between the establishment of the NHS in 1948 and the late 1970s it would be useful to review briefly health service provision before 1948.

HEALTH SERVICES BEFORE 1948

While in many ways the arrival of the NHS was a dramatic transformation from what had gone before, it would be correct to state that in some ways it merely built on ideas and practices which had evolved over a long period of time. The time chart on the next page illustrates the progress made in Britain towards a national health service. The enactment of public health legislation in the 19th century improved sanitation and water supply and led directly to the decline of infectious diseases such as typhoid. At the beginning of the 20th century, the public had to pay for the services of a General Practitioner who could charge what he wished. However, this was, in many cases, beyond the means of people who preferred to seek treatment in a hospital whose out-patient service was free. The National Insurance Act of 1911 provided the free services of a GP and also free drugs to certain groups of employees.

Assessment of Health Care Provision by 1939

The main shortcomings of the pattern of services which existed in 1939 can be summarised as follows.

1 More than half of the population were still not included in the national health insurance system. For those who were not covered and whose income was slightly above the entitlement to free services, a doctor's bill could have severe consequences for the family. Even for those who were covered, however, the insurance did not meet the costs of hospital and specialist treatment.

2 There were, for a number of reasons, marked differences in the quality of care offered by the hospital services. Firstly, some local authorities took their responsibilities for providing hospital services more seriously than others. Secondly, the options for care and treatment offered to patients by voluntary hospitals were generally of a far superior quality than those offered by the local government hospitals. The most pressing problem of all, however, was that the means of financing voluntary hospitals—through fee-payers, charities and street collections—was proving inadequate, and by 1939 more than one-third of voluntary hospitals faced virtual bankruptcy.

The Beveridge Report

In 1941 the Ministry of Health announced as "the objective of the Government as soon as may be after the war", the creation of a comprehensive hospital service available to all. In the same year, Sir William Beveridge was appointed to preside over a committee of civil servants which was to make recommendations on the postwar system of social welfare services. Whilst the argument for state involvement in the provision of health care appeared to have been won, the debate now centred on how this was to be achieved. The Beveridge Report was published in 1942 and its recommendations amounted to a comprehensive attack on what Beveridge called "the five giants" standing in the way of social progress, namely *Want, Disease, Ignorance, Squalor* and *Idleness*. The report, in stating the case for the reform and extension of the social security system, only dealt in detail with the first of these "giants", *Want* (or what we would call today, poverty). Beveridge argued, however, that if people were to be kept out of poverty it would also be necessary for the other four "giants" to be tackled.

In his report, Beveridge attempted to answer what he expected—quite correctly as it turned out—to be the major criticism levelled at his ambitious proposals. This was that they would involve governments in unacceptably high levels of public expenditure, particularly the idea for a state-funded health service. This, Beveridge argued, was to misunderstand totally the nature of the debate. After all, surely the cost of ill health was already being borne by society in terms of lost production and the payment of assistance and relief to those who were idle? A new national health system would make the population healthier which would improve the productive resources of the country and reduce the costs of social security. Moreover, Beveridge expected that the costs to the state of providing this health care would, through time, decline, or at least remain stable, as the backlog of those suffering from ill health was eliminated. The publication of the Beveridge Report was met with widespread public interest and enthusiasm.

Towards a NATIONAL HEALTH SERVICE

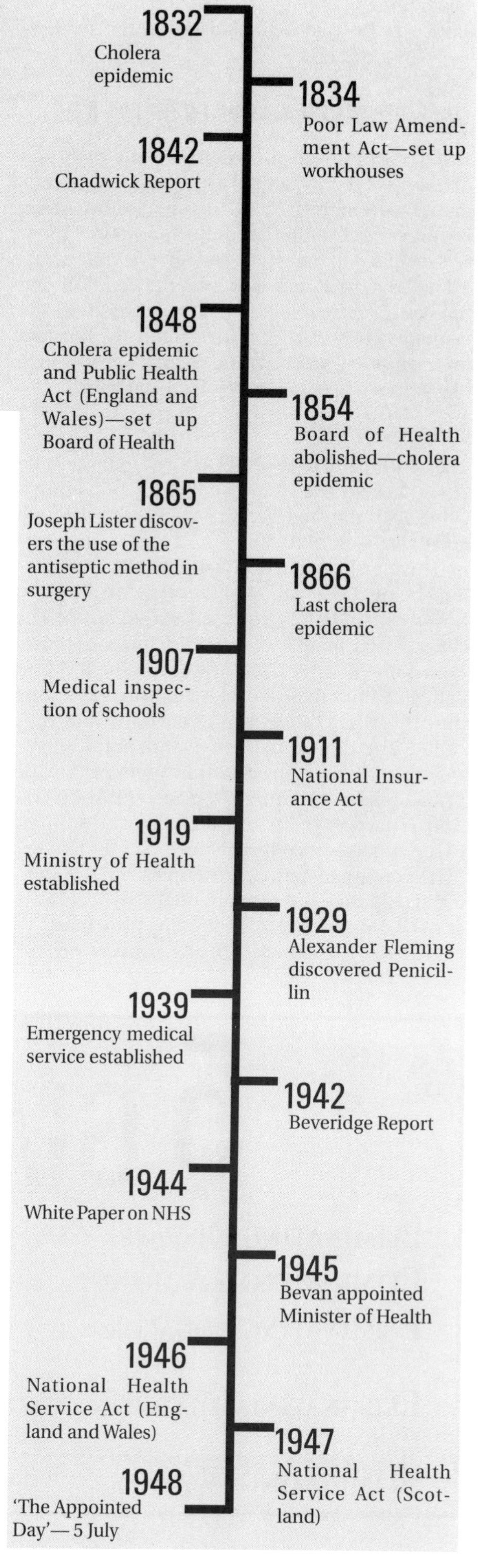

It quickly came to symbolise the hope that post-war British society could become more just and democratic. This popular response ensured a quickening of the pace towards the state's full involvement in a comprehensive scheme of health care.

In 1943, the Coalition government stated its acceptance of the principle of a national health service. This was followed in 1944 by a White Paper outlining the government's proposals on the matter; the Labour government's National Health Service Act of 1946; a separate National Health Service Act for Scotland in 1947; and the establishment of the service itself in 1948.

The 'Appointed Day'

Bevan, the Labour Minister of Health, was forced to make compromises to ensure the support of both hospital doctors and General Practioners.

In the course of his trade-offs between the various competing interests, Bevan was forced to concede much. In his desire to divide opposition within the medical profession, Bevan bought off the hospital consultants and specialists. By agreeing to their demands for private practice and merit awards he had, in his own words, "stuffed their mouths with gold". Although they gained less from the discussions, the GPs were conceded the rights to be paid by a system of capitation fees and of operating from their own practices, thus retaining their semi-independent status. Furthermore, doctors were given the right to participate in the decision making processes within the NHS, something which was not conceded to other health service workers. Of all the many interest groups, the local authorities gained the least, but even they were given control over certain local services.

Thus, the aim of an integrated state-salaried hospital and GP service had been sacrificed and, instead, three nationally directed and financed systems—the hospitals, GPs and local authority services—were set up.

THE FOUNDING PRINCIPLES OF THE NHS

The NHS came into operation on 5 July 1948, and in many ways represented a radical new commitment by the state. With the nationalisation of the hospitals, for example, a completely new element was included in the service. Aneurin Bevan's greatest achievement, however, was the creation of a national health system which was based on the principles of *collective responsibility* by the state for a genuinely *universal* and *comprehensive* range of services with *equal access* for all citizens.

Collectivist

The central aim of the NHS Act was that the state would accept the responsibility for providing a centrally organised health care system through collective action. As was noted earlier, the state had involved itself in health and medical services long before the creation of the NHS. We also saw, however, that the proposed extension of the collectivist principle was met with severe criticism from some quarters. The attitude of the BMA on behalf of the medical profession was, for a long time, hostile to state interference in what they called "the doctor-patient relationship". In the view of one writer, however, the experiences of the British population during the Second World War were crucial in giving respectability and support to the concept of collectivism:

"The pooling of national resources and the sharing of risks were not always practicable nor always applied, but they were the guiding principles."
(R M Titmuss, *Problems of Social Policy* in *History of the Second World War.* UK Civil Series. *1950)*

These same principles of pooling and sharing, which had come to be identified with a nation fighting for its life, were now to become the aims of British domestic policy in general, and the new NHS in particular.

Central government became responsible for both the financial aspects and the direction of policy with regard to the health services. The Ministry of Health, later to become the Department of Health and Social Security, was responsible for the whole of the NHS in England and Wales, while the Secretary of State for Scotland had responsibility north of the border through the Scottish Home and Health Department.

Universal

Another aim of the new NHS was to provide for the whole population a range of health services which were free at the point of use. The previous insurance-based health system meant that access to personal health services without direct payment was limited to those who were covered under the terms of the 1911 National Insurance Act. The problem, as we saw earlier, was that by the 1940s the system only covered about half of the population. By the time of the 1944 White Paper, however, there was a general recognition that in a just and compassionate postwar society, eligibility to use medical services should not depend on either the financial resources of the user, or on an individual's record of contributions to an insurance fund. Instead, it was agreed that this system should be replaced by one which included the principle of being universal. This would ensure that "the availability of necessary medical services shall not depend on whether people can afford to pay for

The 5 GIANTS

ELIMINATING DISEASE	by the creation of a new national health service.
ELIMINATING IGNORANCE	by the introduction of educational reforms.
ELIMINATING SQUALOR	by a programme to improve living conditions, in particular to provide adequate housing.
ELIMINATING IDLENESS	by the promotion of economic policies which would ensure high and stable levels of employment.
ELIMINATING WANT	by reforming and extending the social security system.

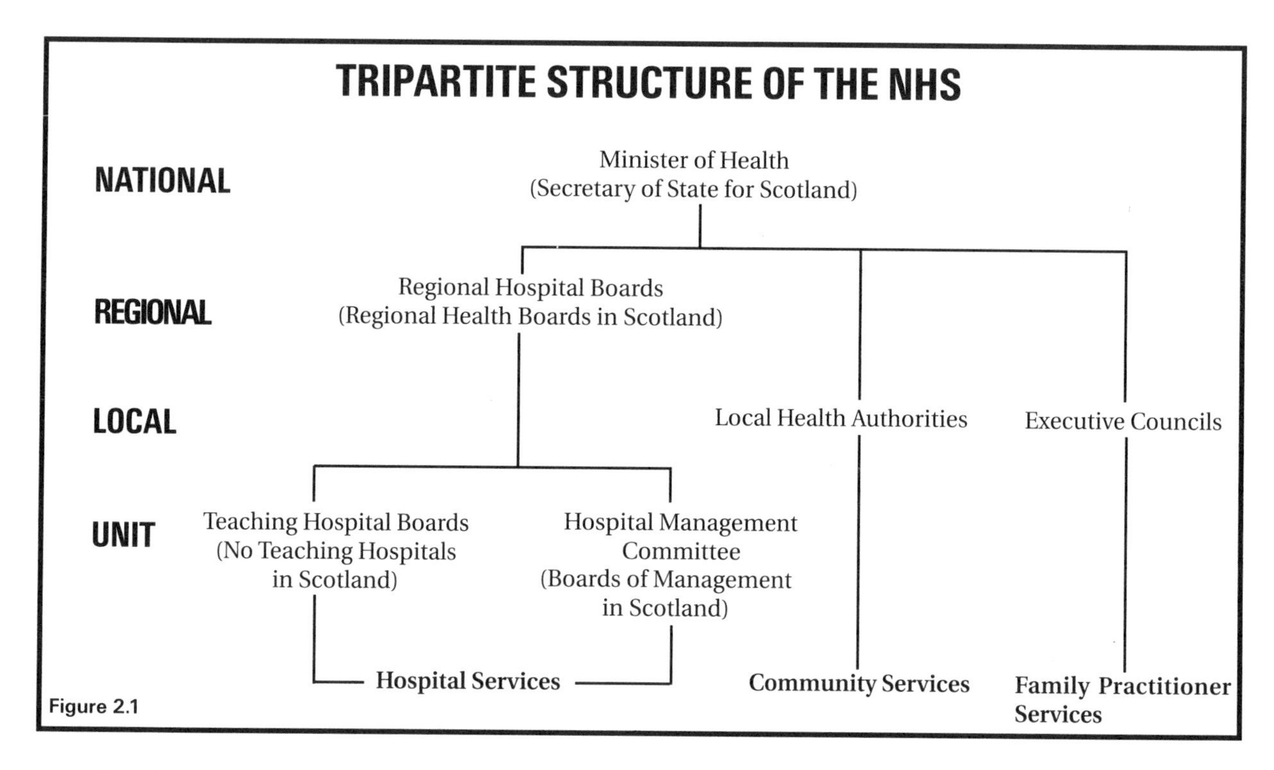

Figure 2.1

them", and that "money should not be allowed to stand in the way of providing advice, early diagnosis and speedy treatment". The revenue of the new NHS was to come, not from an insurance-based system of finance, but predominantly from general taxation.

Comprehensive

The creation of the NHS also meant a commitment to provide "a comprehensive health service for the improvement of the physical and mental health of the people...for the prevention, diagnosis and treatment of illness". Apart from the health care of children, which remained the responsibility of local education authorities, the health care of workers, whose rights were protected by various Factory Acts, and the armed forces which still retained their own health services, the NHS was to be responsible for all aspects of the population's health care. Everyone, however, continued to have the right to obtain health care outside the service, if they so wished.

The administrative structure devised for the NHS was a complicated one. It reflected both the history of state intervention in the health services during the 19th and first part of the 20th centuries, and the final negotiations between the competing political and professional interests which had taken place in the years immediately preceding its inception. The result of this, as we have seen, was that the NHS was divided into three parts.

This 'tripartite' structure was set up throughout the country, although as you can see from figure 2.1, the arrangements for Scotland differed from those south of the border in a number of ways. The tripartite structure, which was to remain in place until the health service was reorganised in 1974, is summarised later in the chapter.

Equality

Finally, the NHS Act expressed commitment to eradicate inequalities in the provision of health care. Prior to the setting up of the NHS, the way the health services had developed meant that there was, in the words of Bevan, "a better service in the richer areas, a worse service in the poorer". Now, though, there was an opportunity "to achieve as nearly as possible a uniform standard of service for all—only with a national uniform standard of service can the state ensure that an equally good service is available everywhere".

The intention, then, was that the quality and the quantity of the health care services available to individuals—the type of treatment, the number of GPs and specialist and consultant posts per head of population, the length of time a person had to wait in order to get treatment and the condition of hospitals—should be the same no matter in which part of the country they happened to live. A unitary service, however, did not materialise.

There were national rules and regulations governing the tripartite health structure, but national equality was to prove to be the most elusive of the guiding principles. This issue will be explored further in Chapter 6.

The Period of Consensus

The period between the establishment of the NHS in 1948 and the late 1970s can be viewed as one of widespread agreement in support of the NHS with a consistency of policy which rose above party ideology and changes in government. The existence of the NHS was accepted by all and its essential features were never seriously challenged. Instead, the debate centred around questions of how best to consolidate the gains made after the launching of the NHS, of how to develop and plan the services, and of how to devise an effective administrative organisation for the system. There was even broad agreement over what came to be seen as the major problems confronting the NHS: finance and effective organisation.

Before looking at these problems, however, an examination of developments in high-technology medicine and advances in drug therapy will highlight the mood of optimism which prevailed in the early years of the NHS.

MEDICAL ADVANCES

The 1950s has been called the decade of the drug revolution. Antibiotics had begun to be introduced in the 1930s, but it was not until the 1950s that they were in everyday use as 'cure-alls' for a wide range of ailments. New potent drugs to control chronic conditions, such as diabetes, were also developed at this time. Indeed, it has been estimated that of all the drugs available to doctors in 1960, 75% did not exist ten years previously.

The enthusiastic belief that the production of new drugs could be the solution to many of the country's medical and social problems seemed to have been borne out. The 1960s will go down in history as the decade of the Pill, when oral contraception offered the promise of safe, easy and full fertility control. It was also the decade when tranquillising drugs, such as Librium and Valium, first came onto the market. These were greeted with enthusiasm by many GPs, who saw them as an instant solution for patients suffering from a variety of mental and psychological problems. They were seen as a safer alternative to barbiturates which, mounting evidence was suggesting, were producing severe addiction side effects.

The unquestioning acceptance of these tranquillisers as panaceas for stress-related disorders can be illustrated by the fact that by 1977 they accounted for a total of 45 million prescriptions signed by doctors.

These new drugs, it was hoped, would help to keep many people out of hospital and might even result in the closure of some, if not all, mental hospitals.

The 1960s and 1970s, however, were to prove to be decades of confusion and contradiction in the field of health care. Despite the hoped for reduction in the need for hospitals, it was also a period which witnessed the development of sophisticated capital-intensive equipment which could only be used within a hospital setting. In the 1960s there was the development of renal dialysis and the treatment of cancer by chemotherapy and radiotherapy. In the 1970s transplant operations for kidneys and hearts were introduced into the NHS and plastic hip replacement surgery became commonplace. Obstetric monitors, cathode tubes, and coronary care units with their isotope scanners were regarded as essential features in all large general hospitals. Patients ranging from premature babies to road accident victims were likely to find themselves wired up to frightening machines with dials and flashing lights, making strange noises and printing out incomprehensible results. High-technology medicine and new drugs, it seemed, were quite capable of conquering the majority of killing and disabling diseases.

The 1960s, however, were also the years of Thalidomide—a sedative which, it turned out, if prescribed to pregnant women could damage human foetuses, resulting in the birth of deformed, sometimes almost limbless, babies. The resulting scandal highlighted the increasingly significant role of the profit-seeking drug industry, with its dubious marketing and trial techniques, as supplier to the state's health service. Similarly, doubts also began to be raised about the use of high-technology medicine.

The heavy expenditure on the new machinery meant that its introduction resulted in fewer resources being allocated to other aspects of the health service. Inevitably, questions over whether this move towards a reliance on new technology was in the patients' best interests began to be asked.

FINANCE

Expenditure

In his Report, Beveridge had estimated that a national health service for Great Britain would cost about £170 million in its first year. Moreover, he had assumed that there was a fixed quantity of illness in the community and that this "pool of illness" would quickly reduce as the new improved system of medical care produced a healthier population. As a result, Beveridge believed that the cost of developing the service would be offset by this fall in demand, and so this £170 million, or its equivalent allowing for inflation, would still be enough twenty years later. The truth of the matter, however, was to prove to be quite different. By

1952/53 the expenditure on the health service had risen to £383 million, which was more than double Beveridge's original estimate. At the time, it appeared that NHS expenditure was out of control.

With the benefit of hindsight, however, it is difficult to see why the founders of the NHS had not forseen this situation. The problem was that they had made the assumption that the cost of the NHS could be calculated by looking at the level of prewar health care expediture, and simply projecting this figure for the post-NHS period. For a number of reasons this method of calculation was to prove unsatisfactory:

1 Prior to the setting up of the NHS, most people had to choose between buying health care or spending their money in other ways, and there is little doubt that charges for medical services often deterred people, particularly those with low incomes, from seeking help. After 1948, of course, charges were abolished and so this element of choice no longer existed. The demand for this new universal health care system, free at the point of access, was far greater than the policy makers had expected.

2 As we have seen, a basic underlying principle of the new system was that "the availability of necessary medical services shall not depend on whether people can afford to pay for them." This commitment was double-edged. Not only did it mean that patients were to get access to the health services without payment, but also that members of the medical profession were to be freed from all financial considerations when advising, diagnosing and treating their patients.

3 The expansion and development of surgery, including new techniques in medicine, inevitably means that there are many more treatable cases than before. More patients reach old age, which in turn means that the health service has to cope with more difficult problems of degenerative and chronic illness. Also, rising public expectations about the contribution medicine can make to us leading longer and healthier lives has meant that demand on the NHS is always likely to be limitless and, no matter how hard it tries, it will never be able to do enough.

Income

Not only did the policy makers miscalculate the expenditure of the NHS, they also failed to anticipate the implications of the system which was chosen to finance it. As we have already seen, an insurance-based system was rejected and, instead, it was agreed that the major proportion of the NHS's income was to come from general taxation. Approximately 88.3% of the National Health Service bill in 1950/51 came from this source, and the figure has fluctuated little since then. One consequence of this decision, however, has been that the NHS has had to compete with other government departments for money allocated to the public expenditure budget.

One way out of this dilemma was for the NHS to find additional means of funding, independent of the Treasury. In the 1950s, charges on dental work, spectacles and prescriptions were introduced. In effect, these decisions breached the original commitment of the NHS to provide a free service for all. Although charges have never contributed more than about 5% to the NHS budget, proposals to find alternative methods of financing the service have persistently reappeared on the agenda.

In these early years then, both governments and interest groups within the NHS were preoccupied with issues dealing with finance. The NHS was consistently unable to keep within its allocated budget and, faced with a government paymaster acting in the interests of the taxpayer, it quickly became associated in the public mind with being an extravagant and inefficient organisation.

It is hardly surprising then, that finance, in terms of both expenditure and income has proved to be the most resilient of all the controversies throughout the history of the NHS.

The Tripartite Structure

Throughout the 1950s and 1960s there was a growing acknowledgement that the NHS's structure was both complex and deficient. The fundamental problem of a system divided into three parts, each controlled by a separate body, was that there was little encouragement for cooperation, let alone integration, between the various services. This, of course, could, and did, have an adverse effect on the quality of patient care.

There were obvious difficulties in providing access to services and continuity of care where there was a gap in, or an overlap of, responsibilities between the branches of the NHS. For example, who should provide ante- and post-natal care? GPs, local authorities and the hospital maternity service could all claim to have a responsibility. In the confusion, a patient might be examined by more than one of these agencies or, more seriously, by none. At the other end of the age spectrum, an elderly patient might require a period of hospitalisation, followed by a spell in a local authority old people's home for convalescence and, finally, care at home from a GP and a domiciliary nurse with the assistance of a home help and the social work department. Clearly, for such a patient to receive adequate continuity of care, there would need to be close coor-

SUMMARY OF THE TRIPARTITE STRUCTURE

1 Hospital services were financed directly by central government.

2 General medical services (now known as family practitioner services), which included GPs, as well as dentists, opticians and pharmacists, remained on a semi-independent contractual basis. They were separately administered by local Executive Councils, with separate funds.

3 Local authority services included district nurses, health visitors, midwives, maternity and child welfare clinics and came under the authority of the Medical Officer of Health in each area. Money for these services was provided partly by central government grants and partly by local rates.

dination between the various services. A change in the structure of the NHS was essential.

STRUCTURAL CHANGE

The 1974 Reorganisation

Between 1948 and 1974 the NHS in England, Wales, Scotland and Northern Ireland had the same basic tripartite structure (see Figure 2.1). When reorganisation came in 1974, different arrangements were made for the four countries. This can be illustrated through a brief examination of the new structures for England and Scotland.

England

The network of 700 authorities—Regional Hospital Boards, Hospital Management Committees, Boards of Governors and Executive Councils—which had been set up in 1948 were swept away and replaced by a much more streamlined structure. 14 Regional Health Authorities were created to act as a link between the Department of Health and Social Security (DHSS) and the 90 Area Health Authorities (AHAs), while the day-to-day running of the health services was to be conducted by District Management Teams (DMTs). Finally, Community Health Councils (CHCs) were set up in each district to "represent the views of the consumer". Opposition from the professional associations meant that it became impossible to integrate them fully into the system.

Scotland

Unlike England, the Regional tier of administration was removed in Scotland. Instead, the Scottish Health Service was administered directly by the Scottish Home and Health Department (SHHD) through 15 Health Boards. In Scotland, then, the Scottish Office department was much more directly involved in the management of the service than was the case in England.

The Secretary of State remained personally responsible for the Scottish health services, with the SHHD within the Scottish Office having charge of the central administration. The Health Boards were directly responsible to the SHHD for the planning and provision of integrated health services in their areas. As you can see from Figure 2.2, the Health Board boundaries closely followed those of the new Regional and Island Authorities set up by the reorganisation of local government in 1975, with the exception that Strathclyde Region had four Health Boards. This meant that the major Health Boards in Scotland were responsible for larger populations than the English District Authorities. It also meant that there was a wide disparity in the responsibilities and resources of the various Health Boards.

Every Health Board had the responsibility of setting up Local Health Councils, which were similar to CHCs in England. In Scotland there was a

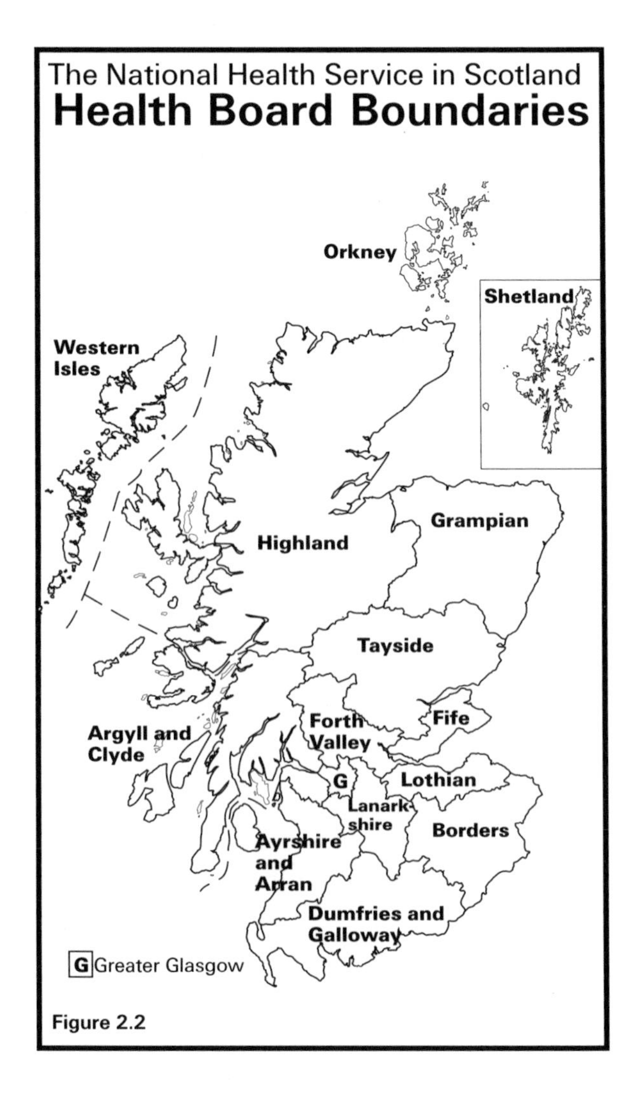

Figure 2.2

close integration of GPs and others providing primary care (such as dentists, opticians and pharmacists) with the rest of the personal health services. There was no separately administered Family Practitioner Committee (FPC) as there was in England. Instead, GPs held contracts directly with the Health Boards.

Aftermath of the 1974 Reorganisation

The underlying aims of the 1974 reorganisation had been to increase the efficiency of the NHS by replacing the tripartite structure with a system which provided effective central control, enabling more rational planning to take place and introducing a greater element of democracy. The new arrangements had barely had time to be put into practice, however, when a wave of dissatisfaction and criticism threatened to overwhelm the system. At a cost of £9 million, reorganisation had done very little to improve relations between the central government departments and those who operated the system at the local level. On the one hand, the local Health Boards and Authorities voiced their resentment over excessive interference from the centre. Parliament, on the other hand, complained about the lack of accountability within the new structure.

As we have seen, this controversy had haunted the NHS since the beginning. The period immediately following reorganisation was one of considerable unrest in the NHS. It was in this context of upheaval and conflict that the government, in 1976, set up a Royal Commission on the NHS. The Commission was asked: "To consider, in the interests of both the patients and of those who work in the National Health Service, the best use and management of the financial and manpower resources of the National Health Service." When the Commission reported in 1979, it made recommendations on a wide range of matters. Its main conclusion was that "there are many aspects of it (the NHS) of which we can be justly proud". Principal among its criticisms, however, was that there was one tier of administration too many in the structure of the system. The Commission's report was published only three months before the General Election which saw the Conservatives, under the leadership of Margaret Thatcher, winning power from Labour.

As we shall see in the next chapter, however, the election of the Conservatives in 1979 was to prove to be something of a watershed in the history of the NHS and was to have far wider implications than mere reorganisational reform.

NHS Problems post 1974

1 The deterioration of the country's economic situation in the mid-1970s had inevitable repercussions on a health system financed almost entirely from taxation. The desire of central government to restrain public spending meant that the NHS was denied the resources it needed to meet the rising demands made upon it and to carry out its policy objectives, such as tackling geographical inequalities in the provision of services.

2 The 1970s witnessed an increase in trade union and professional militancy within the NHS. The 1973 strike of hospital ancillary staff continued after reorganisation and was followed, for the first time in the history of the NHS, by industrial action from junior hospital doctors.

3 The Labour government had pledged in its 1974 manifesto to "phase out private practice from the hospital service". Its attempt to carry out this commitment aroused an angry response and the threat of sanctions against the NHS from the hospital consultants. The reason for this was that such a commitment repudiated the compromise worked out by Bevan in 1946. This issue will be explored more fully in Chapter 8.

Chapter THREE

The NHS under the Conservatives

WE HAVE just lived through a period which is unique in British 20th century history. The 1980s was the first decade in which a single government had remained in power without interruption, and victory for the Conservatives again in 1992 meant that for the first time a party had won four elections in a row. As a result, the Conservative government had a quite unprecedented opportunity to put its ideas into practice. The Conservatives, under the leadership of Margaret Thatcher, were elected into office in 1979 with a manifesto which pledged to control social welfare expenditure by cutting out both waste and bureaucracy and by encouraging the growth of the private sector. They rode to power on the wave of a strong reaction against the trade unions resulting from the so-called 1979 'Winter of Discontent'.

In some ways, however, it was to prove to be a period of contradictions. For all its ideological commitment to the principles of the market, the government did not abandon its collective responsibilities for welfare. Indeed, spending on the NHS went on rising substantially during this time. Throughout the period, the NHS continued to enjoy very strong public support and the political realities of such a situation made it difficult for the government to implement policies which reflected some of its more radical beliefs.

Nevertheless, marked changes did take place in the area of health care. In particular, as we shall see in Chapter 4, the publication, in 1989, of a White Paper called *Working for Patients* was to herald a programme of reforms more basic than any experienced since the beginning of the NHS.

THE 1982 REORGANISATION

The first issue taken up by the new Conservative government was the issue of structural reform. This was a relatively easy option because, as we have seen, the organisation established in 1974 seemed to satisfy no one. The incoming government had also inherited the report of the Royal Commission, which had been set up by the previous Labour government, dealing with the future reorganisation of the NHS. The Royal Commission recommended that the structure be simplified and that it should become more sensitive to the needs of the public.

The new reorganised system came into operation on 1 April 1982. As had previously happened in 1974, the 1982 arrangements were applied in different ways in the various parts of the United Kingdom.

England and Wales

Unlike the 1974 reorganisation which had stressed efficiency and rationality, the emphasis of the new system was on decision making "at the local level —in the hospital and the community" rather than "by any central authority whether at region or in central government departments". Above all else, however, was the intention to simplify the system by removing one of the administrative tiers. The question was, which tier was to go?

While they had their critics, the Regional Health Authorities (RHAs) were reprieved. Instead, the Area Health Authorities (AHAs), the central tier in the 1974 arrangements, were abolished and were replaced by 201 District Health Authorities (DHAs). These DHAs, whose units of management were to be centred on small localities such as the catchment area of a District General Hospital or on a District Service like psychiatry, were to be responsible for both the provision and planning of services. Further, under the new system, Family Practitioner Committees (FPCs) were not only retained despite the Royal Commission's firm rec-

Margaret Thatcher, Prime Minister 1979–1990.

ommendation that they should be abolished, but they were to be given the status of employers in their own right.

Scotland

Since the 15 Health Boards in Scotland undertook both Regional and Area roles, the criticisms regarding too many tiers of management were not present north of the border. Some of the Health Boards, however, such as Greater Glasgow and Lothian, were much larger than any English District in terms of population, while others, such as Highland, were much larger in terms of the area covered. As a result, ten of the Health Boards had set up subordinate Districts after 1974 to help them to administer their areas. In an attempt to simplify this administrative structure, the Secretary of State for Scotland announced that all Districts would be scrapped and would be replaced by a system of Units from 1 April 1984.

SEARCH FOR BETTER MANAGEMENT

Despite the structural changes of 1982, the government remained unhappy about the use of manpower and related resources within the NHS. In particular, it was critical of the management teams of administrators and professionals which, at that time, existed in the service. It believed that these were responsible for long delays in the management process. More importantly, under this consensus management system whereby, in theory at least, a doctor, a nurse, a treasurer and an administrator worked together as a team, no one had the responsibility to put the brakes on the NHS's ever-accelerating costs. As it had done on several previous occasions, the government turned to the private sector for advice and appointed a team of four people, led by Roy Griffiths, Managing Director of the supermarket chain Sainsbury's, to examine the management structure for the NHS in England.

The Griffiths Report

When the team published its report, *NHS Management Inquiry*, in October 1983, it agreed with the government's own diagnosis that there were serious weaknesses in the management structure of the service. The Report noted that the team, all of whose past experience had been limited to the business and commercial world, were shocked to discover that in the NHS "rarely are precise management objectives set; there is little measurement of health output; clinical evaluation of particular practices is by no means common and economic evaluation of these practices is extremely rare". The Report concluded with an interesting phrase which was designed to catch the attention of the media, "... if Florence Nightingale were carrying her lamp through the corridors of the NHS today she would almost certainly be searching for the people in charge".

The report's prescription for this ailment involved a radical departure from the existing system of management by mutual consent. Instead, it recommended the introduction of a professional general management structure at all the various levels in the NHS:

1. At DHSS and government level, the Report argued for the setting up of a Health Services Supervisory Board, with a Management Board under its direction and accountable to it. The Supervisory Board, chaired by the Secretary of State for Health, would be responsible for setting objectives, taking vital decisions, monitoring performance and approving the overall budget and resource allocation. The Management Board, chaired by someone to be appointed specially from the private sector, was to be responsible for the detailed management of the service by carrying out the policies and controlling performance.

2. For other levels of the NHS—regions, districts and units—the Report's recommendation was for the appointment of general managers to improve efficiency. While many of these managers might already be employed in health service administration, some, the Report suggested, might be recruited from the business and commercial world. In addition, the Report, which unashamedly took management structures in the private sector as its model, suggested that the salaries and conditions of service of the general managers should be linked to their performances.

3. Within hospitals, doctors should have a closer involvement in costing and resource budgeting by taking part in management processes.

Reactions to the Report

The published Report created considerable debate and argument. On the one hand, it received a hostile reaction from many of the medical care interest groups. It was criticised as being far too vague and lacking in substance to be regarded seriously as the basis for a major reorganisation of the management process within the NHS. Many others expressed concern at what they saw as the undermining of the system of professional representation in management: nurse managers, for example, were to lose much of the power given to them in the 1974 reorganisation. Most importantly, the Report was criticised for proposing management techniques which were developed in and for a business environment but which would not suit an organisation like the NHS which operates on a quite different basis. It was felt that, if implemented, the proposals outlined by Griffiths would significantly shift the objectives of the NHS. The previous dominant concerns of public good and patient need would become less important than issues relating to efficiency, such as how many patients a hospital could treat and the costs of keeping patients in hospital.

The government, on the other hand, welcomed the Report. In particular, it applauded the various proposals which suggested a move towards a more centralised system. It also approved of the proposal which enabled managers to challenge the professional discretion of nurses, and even consultants, if their working practices ran counter to the aims of obtaining efficiency and reducing costs. It is hardly surprising, then, that the government accepted the Griffiths' recommendations almost in their entirety. The Supervisory and Management Boards were rapidly set up within the DHSS and the English Health Authorities were instructed to appoint general managers at regional, district and unit level by the end of 1985. Further, although the Report referred only to England, the proposals were, in the event, extended to the other parts of the United Kingdom.

Implications of the Report

The main effect of these changes was to introduce into the NHS a form of line management from the top down. Ministers began to take a more direct interest in the appointment of general managers, approving some, vetoing others. Managers running a hospital on short-term (usually three year) contracts began to find that their performance was assessed, not by the Health Authority which employed them, but by the region's general manager above them. A district manager's performance was reviewed by the regional chairperson, who was appointed by Ministers. Thus, a system had been devised which would enable central government to gain tighter control over every level of the NHS.

Conversely, another effect was to encourage a shift towards devolving decision making powers to lower levels. Within certain guidelines and objectives set further up the management line, units of management were given more responsibility to manage their services.

PRIVATISATION

When the NHS was created in 1948, the Labour government allowed the private health care sector the right to continue to operate alongside the public system (see Chapter 2). Until the late 1970s, however, the private sector remained a minor part of total health service finance. Indeed, the Royal Commission on the NHS estimated that at the end of the 1970s the private sector accounted for a mere 3% of total expenditure on health care in the United Kingdom.

There was, however, widespread support for the concept of privatisation within the Conservative government elected in 1979. The assumption was that greater efficiency and improved consumer choice could only be achieved through the economic marketplace.

From 1979, successive Conservative governments showed their enthusiasm for the private health sector in a number of ways. They

- oversaw an increase in the number of pay beds within NHS hospitals.
- encouraged NHS hospital consultants to carry out private work.
- lowered income limits for tax relief on private health insurance.
- supported partnerships between the NHS and the private sector.
- insisted that certain NHS services, such as catering, cleaning and laundry, should be tendered to private contractors.
- introduced higher charges for all forms of dental treatment and brought out new charges for dental and optical checks.
- stimulated the growth in pharmaceuticals bought privately over the counter by introducing a limited list of drugs (which meant that patients had to pay the full cost of those drugs not included on the NHS list) and by regularly increasing prescription charges.

It is not surprising then that, after the Conservatives came to power, there was a very substantial increase in the number of people taking out private health insurance policies. In 1979 5% of the UK population was covered by such policies, but by 1990 this had jumped to over 10%.

DEVELOPMENTS IN PRIMARY CARE

Primary health care centres on general practitioners (GPs) and the different health professionals who work with them in the community, but it also includes dentists, opticians and pharmacists. It has come under close scrutiny by successive Conservative governments since 1979. The reforms they have introduced in this area have had three key aims: to curb costs, to raise standards and to prevent ill health whilst promoting good health.

GPs: The 'Gatekeepers' of the System

It is not difficult to understand why the government regarded GPs as key players in determining demand for health care. The 30,000 or so GPs in the country are often referred to as 'gatekeepers' of the whole health care system. Almost the entire population is registered with an NHS GP, and the average person visits the doctor's surgery four times a year. GPs deal with what they can and pass on to the appropriate specialist the problems which they feel are beyond the scope of GP treatment. The problem for the government was that they had little control over GPs, either in their drug prescribing habits or, more importantly, in the number of patients they referred for expensive hospital treatment.

The reason for this state of affairs is to be found in the way GPs were enlisted in the NHS in 1948. From the outset, although GPs worked for the government, they remained, in effect, independent contractors. Ever since, they had successfully defended their independent status, with the result that they were allowed to spend public money as they saw fit without having to answer to anyone.

Prescribing of Drugs

The first line of attack was to be directed against the traditional right of GPs to prescribe whatever drugs they wished. In November 1984, the government made a complete U-turn and announced that it was imposing a 'limited list' of 30 drugs which doctors would be barred from prescribing on the NHS. Since then this list has been extended further but, even with the country's drugs bill reaching £3 billion in 1993, limiting the rights of doctors to administer the drugs they believe to be appropriate remains a contentious issue. (See article, page 20)

A new GP Contract

The government's intention to carry forward a radical reform of primary health care first became apparent in 1986 with the publication of its Green Paper entitled *Primary Health Care: an Agenda for Discussion.* The proposals which were outlined in this document had two main objectives. The first was aimed at encouraging GPs to offer wider choice and information to patients. The second was an attempt to impose stronger managerial control over the activities of GPs. While these objectives were reaffirmed the following year in the government's White Paper *Promoting Better Health,* a new third principle was added, namely disease prevention and health promotion.

Following the publication of the White Paper, discussions between the government and representatives from the medical profession took place. Despite the granting of some minor concessions, GPs remained extremely hostile to the new proposals. Indeed, in an 82% ballot, family doctors voted 3 to 1 against the proposed new contract. Using its huge majority in the House of Commons, however, the government responded by simply imposing the contract on the GPs. This new contract, which introduced basic changes to GPs' terms of service and system of payment, took effect from April 1990. A closer examination of the terms of the new contract will help to illustrate some of the GPs' concerns.

1 Patient Choice and Information: For the very first time there was a requirement for GPs to provide their patients with practice leaflets which outlined the services they offered, appointment times and out-of-hours cover. Family Health Service Authorities (FHSAs), which replaced the Family Practitioner Committees, were now to publish a local directory of GPs. Moreover, it became easier for patients to change their doctor if they wished and arrangements for making complaints against GPs were simplified.

GPs' criticisms on these aspects were fairly muted. Concern was expressed about the extra paperwork involved in, and the effectiveness of, producing practice leaflets. Furthermore, it was argued, that making it easier for people to change GP was irrelevant as it had been calculated that only about 5% of patients changed their doctors because they were dissatisfied with them.

2 Encouraging 'Good General Practice': The new contract specified the amount of time that GPs were expected to be available for patient consultations. Under the terms of service of the new contract, GPs were obliged, for no extra fee, to offer a consultation to every patient aged 16–74 years who had had no consultation in the previous three years, and to visit all patients over 75 years of age every year.

GPs' criticisms here centred on the requirement to spend time measuring the height and weight of perfectly healthy patients every three years when there were more important duties to perform.

3 Performance-Related Pay: Under the new arrangements, the way in which GPs were paid was radically changed.

a) The balance of GPs' incomes was shifted towards payment per patient, or capitation payments as they are known. Before, 47% of doctors' incomes came from payments related to the number of patients they had on their list, but from 1 April 1990 this was increased to 60%. This change, the government believed, would increase competition by ensuring that those GPs who provided 'good care' would be able to attract and to retain patients and would therefore receive proper financial reward for their efforts.
GPs' criticisms focused on the fear that greater

Health minister denies move to cheaper drugs

THE Government yesterday denied doctors were being forced to prescribe cheaper medicines in an attempt to cut costs.

The health minister Brian Mawhinney rejected drug industry claims that life-saving medicines for premature babies, kidney patients and those at risk from heart attacks and strokes were being restricted.

The country's £3 billion drugs bill was rising at a rate of 12% per annum so it was legitimate for the Government to try to reduce it, Dr Mawhinney said on BBC Radio 4. "But we have never told doctors what they can or cannot do for their patients...patients must get the drugs they need, despite the cost," he added.

However, the Association of the British Pharmaceutical Industry said in a report that the NHS was being "penny wise, pound foolish" by not using higher-priced modern medicines, even when they saved lives and cut more expensive costs such as hospital care.

The report said:

- 3,500 newborn babies die annually in the UK from respiratory distress syndrome, yet less than one in three hospitals routinely offered treatment that stopped the inside of the lungs sticking together when deflated as a life-saving remedy. Many never used it on the grounds of its cost—£700, the equivalent of two days stay in an intensive care unit.
- Less than one-fifth of UK patients with chronic kidney failure and undergoing dialysis were given Erythropoetin to help prevent anaemia. That was less than half the rate in other European countries.
- Six million people suffering from high blood pressure were not receiving medication, while the cost of treating heart attacks and strokes was more than £800 million a year.

Dr John Griffin, ABPI director and author of the report, said: "All the NHS effort is being put into cutting prescribing, not improving it. Time and again we are told this is being achieved without detriment to patient care. But the evidence suggests that British patients are not always getting the best medicines—even where they can save the NHS money in the long run."

Survival rates for heart attack victims would improve if the correct drugs were prescribed, doctors said yesterday in a separate study.

Heart failure costs the NHS about £360 million a year, more than 10 per cent of the total NHS cardiovascular budget, while hospital admissions make up nearly 60 per cent of the cost of heart attacks. Yet drugs account for only 7.5 per cent, according to research published in the *British Journal of Medical Economics*.

The studies, co-authored by a cardiologist and two health economists, show that wider use of the ACE-inhibitor Enalapril could cut the number of hospitalisations by as many as 29,278 a year, saving the NHS £51.2 million.— Press Assoc.

Source: *The Scotsman*, 15 February, 1994.

emphasis on capitation fees would encourage GPs to increase the number of patients on their lists. This, in turn, would mean that doctors would have less time to listen to and identify their patients' problems and to provide counselling and advice. Although a study by Edinburgh University entitled *Quantity, Quality and Queuing* concluded that the best doctors spent most time with their patients, this crucial aspect of primary care was discouraged by the new contract.

b) One of the concessions granted by the government was to introduce a Deprived Practice Allowance. This was an additional payment, over and above the normal capitation rate, which was given for each patient on the list of GPs who worked in practices in deprived areas. The scales of deprivation were based on the Jarman Index (Brian Jarman was Professor of General Practice at St Mary's Hospital Medical School in London). Using ten social factors (see page 22) he produced a deprivation map of the whole country. On the basis of this, he recommended that about 23% of the population should be identified as being in deprived areas. The government accepted the principle, but reduced the number of people covered by the Deprived Practice Allowance to 9% of the population.

GPs' criticisms. The Deprived Practice Allowance was the one universally popular idea in the new contract. However, approximately 14% of the population identified by Professor Jarman as living in deprived areas were omitted from the system by the government. For them, it was claimed, the implementation of the new contract would be likely to result in a worsening level of health care.

c) Specific targets were set for GPs carrying out cervical smears and child vaccinations. Before the new contract, doctors received a payment for each of these individual treatments they carried out.

The new contract, however, stated that they would only receive payments when they achieved particular targets. In the case of cervical smears, if GPs reached 80% of eligible patients they would receive the top rate of payment, while reaching 50% would bring them the lower rate. For child immunisation the top rate would be paid for reaching 90% of eligible children and the lower rate for reaching 70% (see newspaper article page 23). If GPs failed to reach these lower targets, they would receive no money at all for the treatments they had already carried out. The government argued that GPs would have an important incentive to reach these targets and, in so doing, would help to achieve the objective of improving the level of preventative medicine.

GPs' criticisms. There was little argument that GPs who worked in practices in affluent middle-class areas would likely find it relatively easy to follow up their well-motivated patients for screening and that, as a result, the new contract would help them to improve their standards of health care.

In many inner-city areas, however, the rates of screening are, for a variety of reasons, traditionally low. If GPs working in such areas could see very little possibility of reaching the required targets for smears and immunisations, they might well be persuaded to stop doing any of this work altogether and, instead, concentrate on building up the number of patients on their lists. GPs working in marginal areas, on the other hand, might be encouraged to strike certain patients off their lists if they believed that this would improve their chances of reaching their targets.

d) GPs could also earn extra money when they carried out certain duties such as:

- undertaking health clinics for children aged 0–5 years
- providing practice health promotion clinics on subjects such as anti-smoking, alcohol control, stress management, heart disease prevention and diabetes
- carrying out minor surgery within the general practice
- doing their own night visits rather than using a commercial deputising service
- spending time on continuing their education on approved courses would entitle GPs to receive a new seniority allowance.

GPs' criticisms. Many of these payments, for example fees for providing a child health surveillance service and for providing minor surgery services, were welcomed by the profession. The fees for night visits, however, were generally regarded as inadequate and failed to address the problems associated with the provision of out-of-hours work. Indeed, night visits doubled in the first three years following the introduction of the new contract and in 1994 the government responded by proposing that GPs should have the option of refusing to go out and allowing them a day off following night duty.

4 Managerial Control: This was achieved by giving a stronger role to the Family Health Service Authorities (FHSAs) than that given to the bodies which preceded them, the FPCs. GPs had to supply information, such as prescribing arrangements and hospital referral statistics, to FHSAs in the form of an annual report.

GPs' criticisms concentrated on the increasing bureaucracy and paperwork associated with this new duty and on the exercising of managerial influence by FHSAs by the use of cash limited funds as a form of reward or punishment.

The government claimed that the new contract had improved the quality and efficiency of every general practice in the country. Its critics, however, argued that the contract had increased the workload of GPs, while at the same time reducing the time they have to devote to those who are sick. Five years after its introduction, claims and counterclaims on the effects of the GP contract show no signs of lessening.

HEALTH PROMOTION

The first questions which have arisen are what is the meaning of the term health promotion and what is the range of activities to which it refers? Some health professionals give it a very broad-ranging definition claiming that it should refer to any activity which seeks to improve the health position of individuals or communities. Others have attempted to limit the definition by, for example, distinguishing between disease prevention (which deals with individuals or groups thought to be at risk, and aims to conserve health), or by separating health promotion from the established provision of curative and clinical medical services.

The second question, although it is closely linked to the one above, is the debate over what approach would be best to put into action a programme of health promotion. The World Health Organisation (WHO) initiatives stress that social deprivation and differences in material conditions are the key causes of disease and ill health and that government action to tackle social and environmental problems is the solution (the issue of health inequalities will be explored in much more detail in Chapter 6). Government intervention on the scale envisaged in the WHO initiatives, however, did not fit in with the Conservative government's major

THE TEN SOCIAL FACTORS MEASURED IN THE JARMAN INDEX

1. **pensioners living alone**
2. **children under five years of age**
3. **single parent families**
4. **unskilled bread-winners**
5. **unemployed**
6. **overcrowded households**
7. **mobile populations denoted by high removal rates**
8. **households with ethnic minority groups**
9. **over-65s**
10. **lack of amenities**

philosophy of commitment to the free market. As a result, government policies tended to have a much narrower focus by concentrating on changing individual lifestyles.

The Government and Health Promotion

1 Health Education. The importance placed on this area by Conservative governments can be seen from the fact that while £1.6 million was spent on mass media health education campaigns in 1979, this had risen to over £20 million in 1993. Among the campaigns carried out by the government were those concerned with drug and alcohol abuse and preventing AIDS. The government spent £2.5 million on a *Look After Your Heart Campaign* and most of the money allocated to it went on adverts and leaflets telling people to eat better and smoke less.

Criticisms. The assumption behind health education programmes is that individuals are responsible for their own health and that if people are given sufficient information they will be persuaded to adopt a more healthy lifestyle. Some critics have argued, however, that health education campaigns are essentially 'blaming the victim' and ignore wider social influences on health and lifestyle.

Indeed, some recent research has suggested that such campaigns are not effective in promoting better health. A *Health and Lifestyle Survey* published by the Health Promotion Research Trust in 1987, found that people already know what to do in order to stay healthy, what they need is the opportunity or the help to do so.

2 Screening Programmes. The government has also given priority to screening programmes for cervical cancer and breast cancer. By 1991, 70% of all women aged between 50 and 64 had attended screening for both types of cancer.
Criticisms. Although screening cannot prevent women getting cancer it can help to prevent it developing into advanced cancer. Some have argued, however, that screening programmes have had limited benefits—partly because uptake rates tend to be lowest among high risk groups—and that resources used on them would be better utilised in other ways. Recent cases highlighted by the media, for example of women being wrongly diagnosed following screening, have questioned further the value of such programmes.

3 GP-Based Health Promotion. As we noted earlier, many of the proposals in the government's White Paper *Promoting Better Health*, which were introduced through the new GP Contract, were concerned with health promotion. GPs were offered financial incentives for achieving targets for immunisation and cervical cancer screening, and also for other preventative activities such as encouraging the development of health promotion clinics and the provision of health checks. The new contract for dentists which came into effect in October 1990 was designed with similar objectives in mind.

Criticisms. These proposals were broadly welcomed. Some have pointed out, however, that not only are the preventative services offered by GPs unenforceable, but when GPs do carry out this work the patients they see tend to be from low-risk groups and, as a result, much of the doctor's time is taken up with the 'worried well' at the expense of the genuine sick.

4 Prioritising and Target-Setting. In July 1992, the government published a series of documents which were solely concerned with the promotion of health: a White Paper *Health of the Nation*, which related to England, a sister document for Scotland entitled *Scotland's Health—a challenge to us all*, and another one for Wales. These three documents, all of which acknowledged a debt to WHO's *Health For All* initiative, set out a strategy for improving the health of the population by identifying a series of targets, most of which were to be achieved by the year 2000, in five key areas. Of the five priorities identified in *Scotland's Health*, four coincided with areas identified in *Health of the Nation*. The only difference was that dental and oral health was identified as a key area for Scotland rather than mental illness which was identified for the rest of the country (see page 26) for a summary of the key areas and main targets set out in *Health of the Nation*).

Another difference was that while no extra funds were made available for the programme south of the border, £2.2 million was allocated to the programme in Scotland. The health targets were to be implemented through collaboration between

GPs hit bonus figures on health targets

By **Pennie Taylor** Health Correspondent

MORE than 90% of Scotland's family doctors are now hitting health targets set under the GP contract, Health Minister Lord Fraser of Carmyllie announced yesterday.

An increasing number of GPs are receiving bonus payments for meeting objectives set by the Scottish Office for childhood immunisations and cervical smear tests.

The most recent figures—up to October 1992—showed that 93% of GPs reached the higher targets for childhood immunisations and 84% for pre-school booster immunisations. The high levels of immunisations is ensuring rapid progress towards the government's target of 95% uptake of childhood vaccines by 1995.

According to immunisation uptake rates, this target has already been met for diphtheria, tetanus and polio immunisations, while 92% of children have received pertussis (whooping cough) immunisation and 90% measles, mumps and rubella immunisation.

Regarding cervical cytology—smear tests—98% of GPs are reaching the lower target of testing 50% of the eligible women on their lists, and 87% are meeting the higher goal of 80%. Doctors receive cash incentives of £760 a year if they meet the lower target, and £2,280 for the higher.

Welcoming the latest figures, Lord Fraser said: "I am very encouraged that early momentum in the assault on preventable diseases through the GP contract is being maintained."

Source: *Scotland on Sunday*, 31 October, 1993.

various government departments, the NHS, local authorities, voluntary organisations, the Scottish Health Education Board (the Health Education Authority in England), the media and employers.

Criticisms. Although the overall aims set out in the documents were warmly welcomed, a number of criticisms were levelled at the government's programme. These included:

(i) Health problems which have not been specified as priority areas, such as the health of the elderly, asthma and diabetes, may be downgraded and starved of resources.

(ii) The commitment of the government to introduce legislation to help promote health was questioned. Critics pointed to the continuing resistance of the government to the banning of tobacco advertising despite evidence from countries which had introduced such a ban (for example, Norway and Australia) that such action was effective in reducing smoking.

(iii) The most serious criticism, however, was that none of the documents discussed the relationship between poverty and ill health. This was in stark contrast to the WHO's *Health For All* initiative (on which the government's papers were based) which argued that reducing inequalities between social groups had to be central to improving the health of the population. It was argued that by ignoring this and instead stressing personal responsibility, the government's strategy would be ineffective as it failed to tackle the root causes of poor health.

COMMUNITY CARE

The term 'community care' has been used by governments to refer to the policy of caring for people in non-institutional settings—usually in their own homes. The term has tended to be used when speaking about certain groups within society, for example the elderly, the physically disabled, the mentally ill and the mentally handicapped (or, as they are increasingly being referred to, 'people with learning disabilities').

It has long been recognised that services provided for so-called 'dependent groups' such as those mentioned above, have been inadequate and the lack of resources devoted to these services has resulted in them often being referred to as the 'Cinderella services'. Some commentators have argued, however, that the interest shown by the Conservative government in community care was not driven by a concern to improve the quality of services for these groups of people. Rather, it was due to its desire to roll back the frontiers of the Welfare State by shifting the burden of responsibility of care from the state to the individual and to the private sector and, above all, by its declared aim to reduce significantly public expenditure.

The government's main initiative with regard to community care came in 1989 with the publica-

tion of the White Paper *Caring for People*. This was a response to a report published in 1988, which had been prepared by the government's health adviser, Sir Roy Griffiths. The report was called *Community Care: Agenda for Action*. The provisions of *Caring for People* were incorporated into the *NHS and Community Care Act* of 1990. It was envisaged that the reforms would be fully implemented from April 1991 but the government revised its plans and announced that they would be phased in over three financial years, with the bulk of the policies not coming into operation until April 1993.

As we shall see in Chapter 7, the reaction to the government's community care policies has been decidedly mixed.

THE PATIENT'S CHARTER

The introduction, in late 1991, of the Patient's Charter—which was an offspring of a larger initiative, the Citizen's Charter—was an attempt by the government to improve the quality of services from the patient's point of view. The initiative was inspired by the Prime Minister, John Major, and some commentators have claimed that its real significance lay in its attempt to introduce a set of policies which would help to give an identity to 'Majorism' and distinguish it from 'Thatcherism' which had preceded it.

The Patient's Charter set out a number of rights and service standards which patients could expect from the NHS. Seven out of the ten rights simply restated rights which already existed, so only three were new (see page 25). The nine Charter standards were aims rather than rights. One of the standards, for example, stated that there should be a maximum waiting time of 30 minutes at an outpatient clinic. Local charters, which were to set more ambitious and specific targets, were also to be produced. The Charter's ten rights and nine standards came into operation in April 1992. The reaction to the Charter has been mixed. On the one hand, some see the setting down of rights and national standards for the first time as a major step forward. The Patients' Association, for example, was quick to welcome the opportunity it provided for patients to speak up for themselves. Others, however, have argued that the Charter does little to ensure that customers of health services get a better deal. The criticisms levelled at the Charter can be summarised as follows:

(i) Despite the hype which accompanied its introduction, the majority of the public remains unaware of the Charter and of its targets and standards. A MORI poll for the National Consumer Council, released in November 1993, found that 35% of those questioned did not remember hearing about the Charter; only 24% could remember ever having seen a copy, and less than 1 in 5 remembered reading about it.

(ii) Although there is widespread ignorance about the Charter and its contents, it has, some have claimed, unrealistically raised the expectations of an articulate and vociferous minority who have been encouraged to complain about the services they receive. The main victims of these complaints are doctors and nurses who are already stretched to the limit. This willingness to complain seems to be borne out by the Annual Report of the Association of Community Health Councils (CHCs) for 1992–93, which stated that 86% of CHCs had seen a rise in the number of patient complaints, with more than 60% of the CHCs at-

John Major, Prime Minister

tributing the increase to the Charter.

(iii) The ten 'rights' of NHS patients referred to in the document are not rights enshrined in law. Indeed, the Charter itself states they are merely "standards which the government looks to the NHS to achieve as circumstances and resources allow". The Charter did not set up an agency to ensure that the standards were met, so it is difficult to see how patients could have any guarantee that these 'rights' would be forthcoming.

NHS Under the Conservatives

1979	Consultative document *Patients First* recommended reorganisation of the NHS.
1980	Health Service Act passed.
1982	Reorganisation of NHS took effect.
1983	Inquiry into NHS Management (Griffiths Report) published.
	Decision to put out NHS services to competitive tender announced.
1984	Appointment of general managers began.
	Limited drugs list announced.
1987	White Paper *Promoting Better Health* published.
1988	Publication of report *Community Care: Agenda for Action.*
1989	White Paper *Working for Patients* published.
	White Paper *Caring for People* published.
1990	New GP Contract came into effect.
	NHS and Community Care Act passed.
1991	Patient's Charter announced.
	The NHS market came into operation.
1992	White Papers *Health of the Nation* and *Scotland's Health—a challenge to us all* published.
	Patient's Charter came into effect.

THE PATIENT'S CHARTER

Seven existing rights:

1. to receive health care on the basis of clinical need, regardless of the ability to pay;
2. to be registered with a GP;
3. to receive emergency medical care at any time;
4. to be referred to a consultant, acceptable to the patient, when a GP thinks it necessary, and to be referred for a second opinion if the patient and their GP agree this is desirable;
5. to be given a clear explanation of any treatment proposed, including any risks and any alternatives, before the patient agrees to the treatment;
6. to have access to health records and to know that those working for the NHS are under a legal duty to keep their contents confidential;
7. to choose whether or not to take part in medical research or medical student training.

Three new rights:

1. to be given detailed information on local health services, including quality standards and maximum waiting times;
2. to be guaranteed admission for treatment by a specific date no later than two years (later reduced to 18 months) from the day when a consultant places a patient on a waiting list (later changed to when GP refers patient to consultant);
3. to have any complaint about NHS services investigated, and to receive a full and prompt written reply.

THE HEALTH OF THE NATION

Coronary heart disease and stroke (1990 baseline)

- To reduce death rates in the under 65 age group for both coronary heart disease (CHD) and stroke by 40% by the year 2000.
- To reduce the death rate for CHD in people aged 65–74 by at least 30% by 2000.
- To reduce the death rate for stroke in people aged 65–74 by at least 40% by 2000.

Cancer

- To reduce the death rate from breast cancer in the screened population by at least 25% by 2000 (1990 baseline).
- To reduce the incidence of invasive cervical cancer by at least 20% by 2000 (1986 baseline).
- To reduce the death rate for lung cancer under the age of 75 by at least 30% in men and by at least 15% in women by 2010 (1990 baseline).
- To halt the year-on-year increase in skin cancer by 2005.

Mental Health (1990 baseline)

- To improve significantly the health and social functioning of mentally ill people.
- To reduce the overall suicide rate by at least 15% by the year 2000.
- To reduce the suicide rate of severely mentally ill people by at least 33% by 2000.

HIV/AIDS and sexual health

- To reduce the incidence of gonorrhoea by at least 20% by 1995 (1990 baseline) as an indicator of HIV/AIDS trends.
- To reduce by at least 50% the rate of conceptions among the under 16s by 2000 (1989 baseline).

Accidents (1990 baseline)

- To reduce the death rate for accidents among children aged under 15 by at least 33% by 2005.
- To reduce the death rate for accidents among young people aged 15–24 by at least 25% by 2005.
- To reduce the death rate for accidents among people aged 65 and over by at least 33% by 2005.

Source: *The Health of the Nation,* Cm 1986, 1992, pp 18–19.

(iv) A degree of cynicism was expressed about one of the new rights in particular, ie. the right to be admitted for treatment within a maximum of two years after first being placed on the waiting list. In March 1991, 50,000 people were waiting beyond two years, although by the time the Charter came into operation in April 1992 the government claimed that there were now no patients in this category.

Critics stated, however, that over this same period there had been no reduction in the total number of patients waiting for treatment and, indeed, in 1993 the waiting list topped the million mark for the first time. The explanation for this was that while those waiting for over two years had been eliminated, those waiting for less than two years had increased.

Despite these criticisms, however, the government remained committed to the principles behind the Charter. Hospital league tables, covering many of the Charter's standards, were published in June 1994 and it was announced that from April 1995 the Charter was to be extended by setting new improved standards and by redefining how the waiting list was to be measured. Patients would now be entered onto the waiting list as soon as their GP referred them to see a consultant rather than after they had seen one. Also, the two year maximum waiting time was to be reduced to 18 months.

By a long way the most significant of all the changes introduced by the Conservatives resulted from the publication of the White Paper *Working for Patients* in 1989. In the White Paper, the government announced the setting up of an internal health market which separated the demand for health care from supply and allowed competition between providers of services. This is discussed in more detail in Chapter 5.

Chapter FOUR

Setting Out the NHS Market

DURING THE Conservative government's first administration, the private sector was encouraged, the structure of the NHS was tinkered with, tough financial controls were imposed and a new management system was introduced. Despite these changes, however, the Prime Minister seemed extremely reluctant to sanction radical surgery on the health care system. Indeed, during the 1983 General Election campaign, amid growing concerns about Conservative intentions, Mrs Thatcher felt compelled to pledge that, "The NHS is safe with us. The principle that adequate health care should be provided to all, regardless of ability to pay, must be the foundation of any arrangements for financing the NHS." Critics might worry that only "adequate" health care had been promised, and that different "arrangements for financing the NHS" had not been dismissed, although apart from the imposition of the new GP contract, Margaret Thatcher's second administration did, in fact, remain remarkably timid in its dealings with the NHS. Further, in their manifesto for the 1987 General Election, the Conservatives included radical proposals for education, housing for the inner cities and local government taxation, while the NHS received only scant attention.

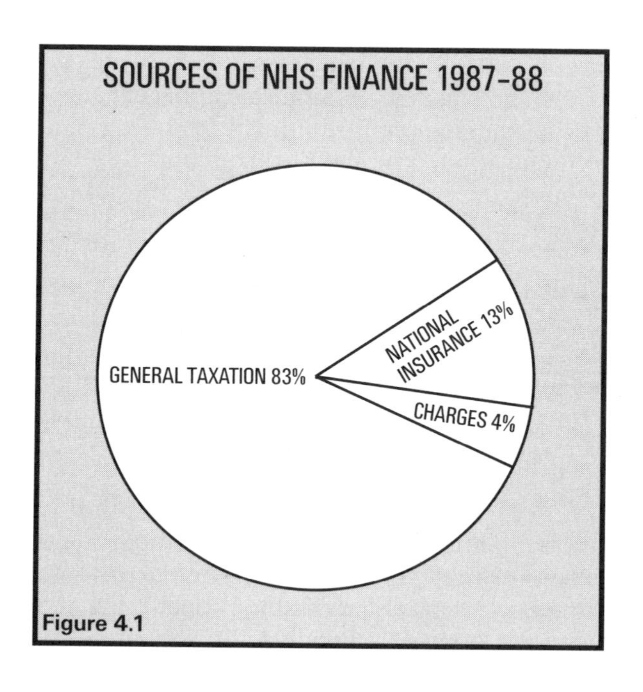

Figure 4.1

All this was to change, though, in a matter of a few months following their electoral success. The cause was to be the same issue which has continued to haunt the NHS since the beginning—finance.

CRISIS IN THE NHS

The Problem

The NHS's sources of finance in 1987–88 are illustrated in Figure 4.1. Between the years 1979 and 1988, a period of financial stringency, the government had increased spending on the NHS by 39% in real terms, ie. over and above inflation.

Despite government claims of 'growth' in and 'increased funding' of the NHS under its care, the public perception was of 'cuts' and 'underfunding'. The explanation for this apparent contradiction was that while government spending on the NHS did, in fact, rise faster than general inflation, the tendency was for the NHS to have a much higher rate of inflation than for the economy as a whole. The reason for this was due to a combination of factors:

1 The growing numbers of elderly people had (as we shall see in Chapter 7) quite profound implications for the NHS. Health costs for the over 75s, for example, were about seven times more than those for the population as a whole.

2 The cost of drugs, medicines and new health technology were all increasing. Also, health service resources were increasingly being taken up by the use of high cost hospital-based treatments.

3 The pressures to meet specific government policies, such as developing community care for the elderly, the mentally ill and the handicapped required more money to be spent.

4 75% of the total NHS budget was spent on salaries. Although many health service workers were very poorly paid, during the decade most of them received pay rises which ran ahead of the general inflation rate. The government, however, failed to fund fully NHS pay rises and Health Boards and Authorities were expected to make up the balance from within their own budgets.

Even the government acknowledged that, to meet

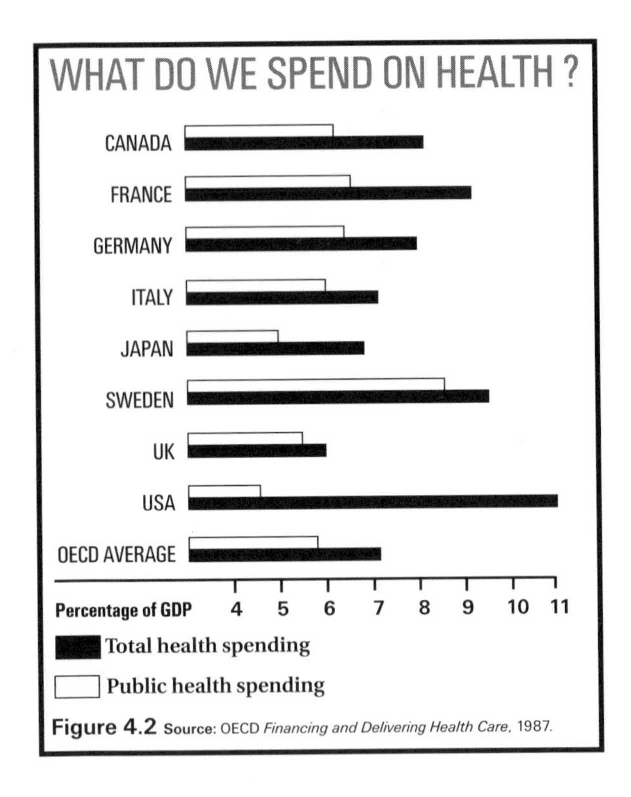

Figure 4.2 Source: OECD *Financing and Delivering Health Care*, 1987.

these pressures of rising prices and pay in excess of the general inflation rate, the resources of the NHS needed to grow by 2% in real terms every year.

The government, however, argued that it did not need to give the NHS this extra 2% every year to enable the service to grow. Its reasoning for this hinged on two separate but related arguments. Firstly, Ministers continually boasted that statistics clearly demonstrated that during the 1980s the NHS had become a more productive organisation. For example, in evidence given to the 1988 enquiry by the House of Commons Social Services Committee, it was shown that heart operations increased from 27,200 to 43,000 between 1980 and 1985, while hip replacement operations increased from 44,800 to 53,000. Moreover, there were more day cases and patients were being discharged from hospital earlier. Secondly, it was emphasised that 'cost improvement programmes' had enabled the service to generate extra funds. It was claimed that the NHS had been able to save money by such measures as putting their catering, cleaning and laundry services out to competitive tender (see Chapter 5), by the more efficient purchasing of their supplies and by the rationalisation of their services, such as the closing down of small local hospitals.

While these two factors could not be dismissed out of hand, critics argued that there were flaws in the government's line of reasoning. For instance, forcing patients to be discharged earlier from hospitals might well enable more patients to be treated, but it might also reduce the quality of their treatment. Indeed, the government's statistics did not show how many of the extra patients the NHS was now treating were those who had to be readmitted to hospital due to having been discharged too early. In 1988 the All Party Social Services Committee (which had a majority of Conservative MPs) calculated that if the NHS was to be allowed to achieve its annual growth of 2% it had been underfunded by the government to the tune of nearly £1.9 billion since the start of the decade. This was even after allowing for the savings from the 'cost improvement programmes'.

As the debate quickened, critics began to argue that if international comparisons were taken into consideration, the case that the UK was spending too little on its health care became more evident. Figure 4.2 shows how health expenditure in the UK compared with that of other Organisation for Economic Cooperation and Development (OECD) members. As you can see, public spending on the NHS in 1987 was 5.3% of our Gross Domestic Product (GDP), which was below the average for OECD countries. When private spending was added in, however, the position became even worse. As we shall see in Chapter 5, the UK had a growing private health sector, but it was still relatively small and contributed less money than the private sector in any other OECD country.

Pressure for Action

This debate over NHS funding was, of course, nothing new. What was different about the crisis in 1987–88, though, was the scale and intensity of the controversy. National newspapers and television programmes devoted considerable space and time to reports of patients queuing for months and even years with so-called non-urgent but often very painful complaints, hospitals cancelling operations due to a shortage of nurses, lack of finance forcing hospitals to close down wards and nurses picketing Parliament to draw attention to the problems of the NHS. At the end of 1987, headline stories about a number of babies, whose routine hole-in-the-heart operations had to be postponed by the Birmingham Children's Hospital because of staff shortages, moved the nation.

Heated comments over the financing and future of the NHS did not only come from the media. The BMA argued that the NHS required additional resources to avert the funding shortfall and the President of the Institute of Health Service Management pleaded for a radical review of the NHS. More ominously, the Presidents of the non-political Royal Medical Colleges issued an unprecedented and critical joint statement on the crisis calling "on the government now to do something to save our National Health Service, once the envy of the world." In the House of

Commons, there were five full debates on the NHS, numerous Early Day Motions and adjournment debates and Prime Minister's Question Time seemed to be devoted almost entirely to the debate. The NHS, which was due to celebrate its 40th anniversary in 1988, had become *the* issue of Mrs Thatcher's third term of office, and one which the government was finding increasingly difficult to sidestep.

THE NEW NHS

Working for Patients

Although pre-empted by what turned out to be a series of extremely accurate press leaks, the government's long-awaited plans for the reform of the NHS were officially unwrapped with the publication of its White Paper, *Working for Patients*, on 31 January 1989. This 100 page document was launched in a blaze of publicity, involving a television link-up between Ministers in London and health specialists in the regions. A video for health service employees was also produced. The cost of the exercise was £1.75 million. The Prime Minister stated that the proposals were "the most far-reaching reform of the NHS in its 40-year history" and the government clearly believed that it was important to get its message across successfully to both the health service interest groups and the electorate.

Despite pleas from right-wing 'think tanks', such as the Adam Smith Institute and the Centre for Policy Studies, to take the opportunity of the Review to dismantle the NHS, the government, in the face of continuing public support for the basic founding principles of the service, stopped short of such drastic surgery. Indeed, *Working for Patients* clearly reaffirmed the NHS as an overwhelmingly tax-financed system, universal in its scope and mostly free at the point of use. In announcing his prescription to the Commons, the Health Secretary, Kenneth Clarke, claimed that the proposals merely reflected a change of pace, not of fundamental direction.

The main proposals outlined in the White Paper were concerned with how the services were to be delivered rather than with finance and, in this respect, they did mark a radical break with the past. Relying on key elements of its own political philosophy, the government added the principles of competition and market forces onto the original principles of the NHS. The underlying idea was to separate the purchaser and provider roles with the new system working like a market with buyers (or purchasers) and sellers (or providers). Fundamental to this so-called 'internal market' was the idea that money would follow patients.

'I never dreamed the bed shortage was so acute.'

The assumption was that the internal market would make the service so efficient that financial crises would become a thing of the past. It would also help to increase consumer choice or, as Margaret Thatcher stated in the foreword to *Working for Patients*, it would "bring all parts of the NHS up to the very high standards of the best...".

As soon as *Working for Patients* emerged in January 1989, all the health service trade unions launched campaigns against the government's proposed changes. 'Hands off our health service' campaigns were established across the country, linking hospital workers with local communities. The White Paper had succeeded in uniting all of the branches of the medical profession against it. The most highly publicised campaign was conducted by the BMA. Matching almost pound for pound the government's expenditure on selling its changes, the BMA countered by organising a series of regional roadshows and producing videos, leaflets, posters, and briefings for both its members and the media. Using its nationwide network of sympathetic doctors to relay its message—the 30,000 or so GPs alone see some 5 million patients a week—the BMA gained a clear lead in the debate.

Together with parallel changes to community care planned by the government (these are discussed in Chapter 7), the proposals outlined in *Working for Patients* were incorporated into the *NHS and Community Care Bill*. Despite the success of the BMA's campaign in winning public support, and the fierce hostility from the opposition parties, the government was able, due to its large majority in the House of Commons, to steer its legislation through Parliament. The Bill received Royal Assent in June 1990.

There were clear signs, however, that the

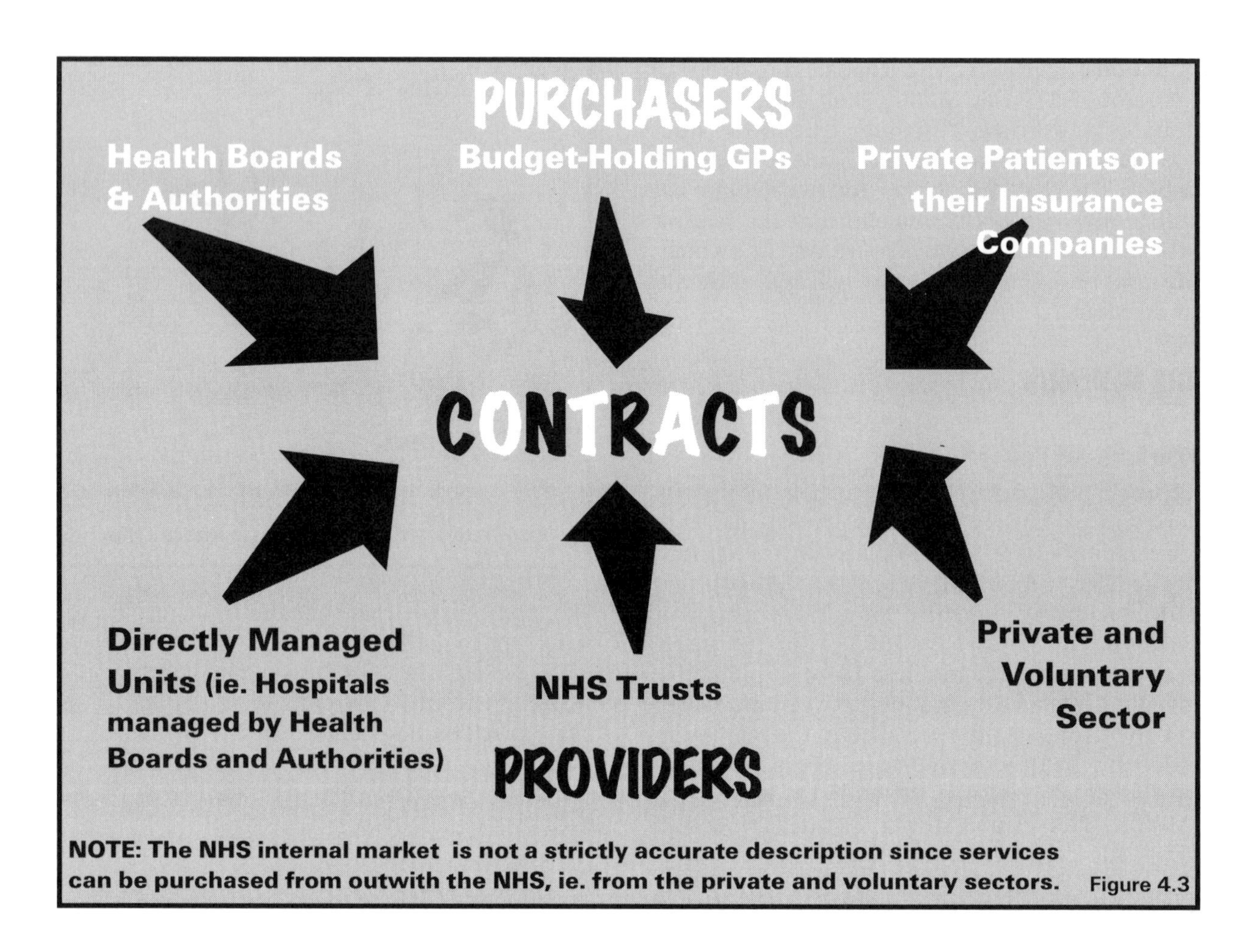

NOTE: The NHS internal market is not a strictly accurate description since services can be purchased from outwith the NHS, ie. from the private and voluntary sectors.

Figure 4.3

government was beginning to recognise the possible political cost of pursuing its radical reforms. It started to promote the idea that the changes represented a natural progression from earlier efforts to improve efficiency, rather than a radical break with the past; in other words, the reforms should be viewed as evolutionary rather than as revolutionary. The language of the market, which had been so prominent in *Working for Patients*, was quietly dropped and Ministers began to tell us, for example, that different parts of the NHS would not 'compete' but would 'contract' with each other.

THE NEW STRUCTURE

The general principle behind the structural changes was the same for the whole country. The main idea was that there should be a 'chain of management', from the top downwards, similar to that in industrial companies. The hope was that this would tighten central control over the NHS's policies and priorities. As with previous reorganisations, however, there were differences in detail in the proposals north and south of the border.

In **England** the top level was a new NHS Policy Board, chaired and appointed by the Secretary of State for Health. Its function was to determine the strategy, objectives and finances of the NHS in the light of government policy. Also, it was to oversee the next level, the NHS Management Executive, chaired by a Chief Executive appointed by the Secretary of State. This was to be responsible for all day-to-day operational matters in the NHS. The 14 Regional Health Authorities remained in the system, although it was later announced that they were to be reduced to 8 before being transformed, in 1996, into regional offices of the NHS Management Executive. The 190 District Health Authorities were also retained, although they were to have their responsibilities slimmed down, delegating many of their operational functions to hospitals. Subsequently, it was announced that from 1996 District Health Authorities and Family Health Service Authorities (formerly known as Family Practitioner Committees) were to merge. In both Regional and District Authorities, membership places which had previously been reserved for local government, trade unions, medical and nursing nominees were done away with. Local community interests continued to be represented by Community Health Councils.

In **Scotland** the new management structure was headed by a Chief Executive, who was responsible for overall management and efficiency and who reported directly to the Scottish Secretary. The 15 Health Boards remained, but the number of members was reduced with a greater emphasis being given to managerial and executive skills and less to their role as representative bodies for local authority opinion. The Health Service Policy Board was abolished, and was replaced by a new Advisory Council made up of Health Service management, professional and other staff, the universities, the private health sector and other related interests. Its function was both to advise the Minister and to offer guidance to the Health Boards. The Local Health Councils remained in the system.

Timetable for Reform

The original timescale set by the government, with contracts for all services to be in place by April 1991, was very ambitious. As we have seen, however, the reforms remained highly unpopular with both the public and the medical profession. In an attempt to placate the opposition—and to keep the NHS out of the newspaper headlines in the period leading up to the general election—the government announced that the pace of the reforms was to slow down. 'Timetable for Reform', shows the reforms were introduced in Scotland a year behind the rest of the country.

Separation of Purchaser and Provider Functions

Central to the philosophy behind the reforms was the creation of what became known as the NHS internal market. This is not, however, a strictly accurate description for, as we shall see, it was never intended that competition was to be restricted to the NHS; the private and voluntary sectors were also to be involved.

The essential first step for the operation of this so-called internal health market was the separation of purchaser and provider roles and the creation of a network of buyers and sellers of health care. Under the reforms, Health Boards (in Scotland) and Authorities (in England), Fundholding GPs and private insurance companies became the buyers, purchasing care for their patients. The hospitals, whether trust-holding, directly managed or from the private sector became the sellers, competing with each other to provide the various services for patients. The operation of the internal market is illustrated in Figure 4.3.

Purchasers are not restricted to buying services from providers in their own area, but can also approach providers in other Health Board or Authority areas or, indeed, providers outside the NHS altogether. In other words, a Health Board has the option of buying services from its own directly managed hospitals, from another Board's hospital, from an NHS Trust hospital or from a private hospital. It is through this process, the government claims, that money follows the patient. Contracts provide the link between the purchasers and the providers. The purpose of these contracts is to

TIMETABLE FOR REFORM

1988

- Review of NHS announced by Margaret Thatcher

1989

- *Working for Patients* published
- NHS Policy Board and Management Executive in England set up
- Chief Executive and Advisory Council in Scotland established
- First self-governing hospitals identified
- First additional consultants posts created
- Audit Commission begins work

1990

- 'Shadow' boards of first group of self-governing hospitals draw up plans
- Health Authorities and Boards and FPCs reconstituted
- Regions pay for work done for each other

1991

- First hospitals become self-governing
- First GP practice budget holders begin operating
- Indicative drug budget scheme starts
- Authorities pay for work done for each other

1992

- First NHS Trusts and GP Fundholders in Scotland
- Re-election of Conservatives under John Major

1993

- Second wave of NHS Trusts and GP Fundholders in Scotland. Third wave in England established

1994

- Third wave of NHS Trusts and GP Fundholders in Scotland. Fourth wave in England established

PERCENTAGE OF POPULATION COVERED BY GP FUNDHOLDERS 1993/4 AND 1994/5

Health Board	1993/4	1994/5
Argyll & Clyde	8.6	8.6
Ayrshire & Arran	6.8	8.7
Borders	6.8	15.5
Dumfries & Galloway	0	4.8
Fife	8.8	8.8
Forth Valley	4.6	11.7
Grampian	49.2	60
Greater Glasgow	4.4	11
Highland	6.1	14.3
Lanarkshire	16.8	30
Lothian	10.3	19
Orkney	0	0
Shetland	0	0
Tayside	18.5	21.2
Western Isles	0	0

Table 4.1

specify cost, quantity and quality (for example, clinical standards, waiting times, staffing levels, cleanliness and patient satisfaction) with regard to the services being provided.

In theory at least, therefore, the purchasers have a great deal of control over the standards of services which they buy.

GP Services

1 *Fundholding Practices.* One of the most controversial changes was to allow GPs to apply to take control of their own budgets. Before the reforms, most of the services used by GP practices were bought and paid for by the Health Board or Authority from their overall budget. Now, however, practices over a certain size are encouraged to become fundholding practices which are allocated a sum of money at the beginning of the financial year from the Health Board or Authority budget to buy a defined range of services for the patients.

The range of services included in the fundholding scheme has been extended. Originally, the services comprised outpatient treatment, diagnostic tests such as X-rays and laboratory tests, and some non-urgent operations or day treatment. In 1993, however, community services such as district nursing, health visiting, chiropody and dietetics were added to the scheme and more recently a number of practices have been taking part in an experiment testing the viability of extending the services even further.

The patients of non-fundholding GPs can only be referred to services with whom the Health Board or Authority has placed contracts. However, GPs in budget-holding practices can buy services for their patients wherever they choose, including the private sector. If fundholding practices save any money from their budgets they can use it to improve their practices.

The size of practices eligible to apply to become fundholders has also been widened since the reforms were introduced. *Working for Patients* had specified that only practices with 11,000 patients or more could apply to take control of their own budgets. This list size was later reduced to 9,000, then to 7,000 and, from April 1995, to 5,000 with a new form of 'community fundholding' enabling practices with just 3,000 patients to buy community health services.

By the end of 1994 nearly 30% of GP practices in England had become fundholders. Although only 10% had joined the scheme in Scotland by the end of 1994, as you can see from Table 4.1, there was a wide variation in the take-up rates by GPs in the different Health Board areas.

2 *Indicative Drug Budgets.* Drugs are the single largest item in the family practioner services budget. In an attempt to reduce this expenditure, GPs who are not in fundholding practices have been give a prescriptions target, known as an 'indicative' drug budget. This budget, or target, depends on the number of patients on the practice's list and is weighted for factors such as the number of elderly patients and local social conditions. Overspending on the target can lead to a large fine being imposed on the GP practice.

NHS Trusts

Another controversial proposal was the encouragement of hospitals to become NHS self-governing Trusts, popularly referred to as 'opting out'. In *Working for Patients,* short-stay hospitals with more than 250 beds were identified as suitable candidates for self-governing status but, as time passed, it became clear that all services (ie. community services, mental health and ambulance services) were eligible.

Compared to GP Fundholding, the NHS Trust scheme has been implemented at a much faster pace. 57 units were granted trust status in the first wave in England in April 1991, while in Scotland, where the reforms were introduced in April 1992, only two units—South Ayrshire Hospitals and the Forresterhill group of hospitals in Aberdeen—opted out in the first wave. By April 1995, however, over 90% of all services in England had become Trusts while in Scotland all but one of the hospitals on the mainland (the exception being the State Hospital at Carstairs) were managed in this way.

Each NHS Trust is run by a Board of Directors consisting of a Chairperson, 5 non-executive members (lay people) and 5 executive members (certain managers employed by the Trust). The chairperson and the 5 non-executive members are appointed by the government while the executive members are appointed by the non-executive members. The Board is responsible for determining overall policy, while day-to-day management is the responsibility of the general manager. The NHS Trust is expected to run its own affairs on business lines, operating in much the same way as a private hospital.

When a unit becomes a Trust it is allocated the assets of the unit, namely the land, building and equipment. It then has to earn its revenue from the treatment/services it can sell to Health Boards or Authorities, GP Fundholders, private hospitals, private patients and possibly other Trusts. Trusts are expected to make a profit to stay in business. Opted-out hospitals have a range of freedoms not available to hospitals directly managed by a Health Board or Authority). In practice, however, some of these freedoms have proved to be somewhat false. For example

- the government stipulated that when Trusts borrow money they must do so on the best terms available which, in effect, means that they have to borrow from the government rather than from the private sector;

- the amount that Trusts can spend on capital development was limited;

- the freedom of Trusts to set their own pay and conditions was modified, for example by a rule that they must adhere to national pay agreements for junior hospital doctors;

- although Trusts can set their own priorities, they must also ensure that they continue to provide the essential 'core' services for the local population (such as accident and emergency departments) where no alternative exists.

Medical Audit

Working for Patients stated that "medical audit" was to be "a fundamental principle of the review". This was to involve creating a structure where the quality of medical care would be analysed, including procedures for diagnosis, treatment and the use of resources.

Medical audits, or checks on the quality of medicine and surgery, are carried out by other doctors, although management has a responsibility to ensure that effective audit systems are in place and that each medical team is regularly reviewed. Review findings in individual cases are confidential, but the general results of medical audit are made available to management and the lessons learned are published more widely. GPs too are required to audit their care. For example, their desk computers can give them comparisons of their own prescribing costs with local and national averages.

Finally, the Audit Commission, which was already responsible for local authority spending, has been given the additional duty of ensuring that the various NHS bodies are giving better value for money.

The Private Sector

Working for Patients welcomed the private health sector's increasing contribution to patient care. In an attempt to boost its role in providing services, the government introduced income tax relief on private medical insurance for the over-60s. The White Paper also urged greater partnership between the NHS and the private sector. This was to include an extension of competitive tendering, and more joint ventures between the two sectors. These issues are examined in more detail in Chapter 5.

Patients

As the title of the White Paper suggests, the declared aim of the reforms was to make the health service "a place where patients come first". Over and above this general principle, however, the White Paper outlined several specific measures which it wanted hospitals to undertake to improve patient care. These included offering an individual appointment system; more pleasant waiting areas; easy to understand information leaflets about facilities; easier ways of making suggestions and complaints; clear and sensitive explanations to patients about treatment; rapid notification of test results; and a wider range of extra amenities which could be paid for, such as single rooms, personal telephones, televisions and a choice of meals.

THE NEW NHS: SURGERY OR BUTCHERY?

The old NHS was a much admired institution which, compared to other advanced countries, delivered health care services in a very cost-effective way. There was general agreement, however, that the service was not perfect. Some of the problems from which it suffered included under-investment, inadequate quality assurance, little thought for patient comfort, wide variation in performance, differences in waiting times for non-emergency treatment, significant differences in costs for identical operations and contrasting rates in GPs' referrals to hospitals and in their drug prescribing habits. What is less clear, however, is whether the reforms have made the NHS better or worse.

On the one hand, supporters of the government's reforms have argued that the addition to the old system of the new element of competition and a limited marketplace has helped to boost efficiency, increase productivity, improve decision making and provide better services for patients. On the other, critics have argued that the reforms have failed to address the central problem of the NHS, which remains a lack of funds. They also say that the main effect of the changes has been to create a two-tier health service which is threatening both the principle of equal treatment on the basis of need and the means of achieving it.

The debate is perhaps best considered by examining the arguments for and against the elements of the reforms which have caused most dispute namely:

- the division of purchasing from delivery functions
- the introduction of budget-holding for GPs
- the creation of NHS Trusts.

This is done on the following pages.

THE PURCHASER-PROVIDER SPLIT

Arguments For

1 Before the reforms were introduced, the providers of health services held the dominant position within the NHS. This was particularly true of doctors working in the acute hospital sector who were able to use their favoured status to win an unequal share of resources for their services.

The separation of the responsibility for purchasing and providing health services, however, has helped to shift the balance of power in favour of purchasers. Priorities are now being determined by Health Boards/Authorities and GPs, with the result that previously neglected services (such as physiotherapy and chiropody) are being given increased resources. This change in prioritising is allowing resources to be used in a way which better meets the needs of patients.

2 The introduction of competition into the system has encouraged purchasers to buy services from producers who offer the best value for money. This has meant that purchasers have begun to switch their contracts towards low-cost services, such as day surgery, and also towards low-cost providers, such as primary care. The shift in service provision towards primary care has allowed resources to be targeted towards the promotion of health as set out in *Health of the Nation* and *Scotland's Health—a challenge to us all.*

3 In a system in which money follows the patients, providers have to compete with each other for resources from purchasers. In order to win these resources, providers must draw up contracts which specify cost and volume of services, along with a range of quality standards.

As a result, providers have become more accountable to purchasers and have been forced to improve their performance by increasing their efficiency and the quality of their services.

Arguments Against

1 The introduction of the internal market, with its fragmented structure of buyers and sellers of health services at the local level, has made it more difficult to plan from the centre. The concern is that without adequate central planning, enormous differences in the quality of services will arise throughout the country. If this were to happen, the principles on which the NHS was founded would be weakened.

2 Despite the government's claims that the reforms have encouraged money to follow patients and that they have improved consumer choice, the evidence so far suggests that this has not happened. The internal market is based on the contracts negotiated between purchasers and providers. The effect of this is that patients are following the money rather than the other way around. Furthermore, if a purchaser does not have a contract with a particular provider, the purchaser's patients cannot receive treatment from that provider. Consequently, the freedom of patients to choose providers has been considerably restricted.

NHS Trusts

A Trust can:

- Own its own assets, aquire new assets and raise money by selling assets
- Retain any profit it makes to finance future investment projects
- Borrow money from the private sector as well as from thegovernment to use for investment purposes
- Employ its own staff and determine its own staffing levels
- Set its own rates of pay and conditions of service
- Determine its own priorities, for example expand a speciality which it believes will be particularly profitable
- Manage its own affairs without having to refer to the Health Board or Authority

3 There is concern that purchasers are awarding contracts on the basis of increased quantity and lower prices rather than on the quality of standards being offered. If this is allowed to continue, low-cost (and probably low quality) providers will emerge as the winners, while high-cost (and probably high quality) providers will lose out.

4 The internal market based on contracts between purchasers and providers is a much more expensive system to run than the one it replaced. The Labour Party claimed that the government wasted nearly £2 billion on the NHS shake-up—money which, it argued, could have been spent on doctors, nurses and medical equipment. Much of this cost was due to the need to invest in management systems and personnel. Indeed, the number of managers and administrators rose by 36,000 between 1989 and 1992, compared with 3,000 more doctors and 26,000 fewer nurses.

FUNDHOLDING GPs

Arguments For

1 Since GP fundholders are not bound by where the Health Board or Authority place their contracts, they have a wider choice than their non-fundholding colleagues of where to send their patients for treatment. GPs know their patients better than administrators from the Health Board or Authority, and so they are the most appropriate people to negotiate contracts for patients.

2 GP fundholders have been able to use their purchasing power to negotiate favourable contracts with hospital managers and consultants on behalf of their patients. As a result, their patients have benefited from shorter waiting times for non-emergency care and there has been improved communication between hospitals and GPs.

3 Fundholders are expected to stay within their budgets and this gives them a stronger incentive than non-fundholders to think about the costs of their decisions. For example, since fundholders have to pay for many of the hospital services used by their patients, unnecessary referrals to hospitals are likely to become a thing of the past. Consequently, the fundholding scheme is helping the NHS to make great savings.

4 GP fundholders can use any money they save from their budgets to improve services within their practices. Many fundholders have used their savings to provide a range of new services such as physiotherapy, stress counselling, dietary advice and midwifery. Thus, the fundholding scheme (along with the changes brought in by the GP Contract of 1990) is consistent with the government's health promotion strategy and its declared intention to shift more hospital services into the community.

Arguments Against

1 The fundholding scheme has, in a number of ways, helped to create a 'two-tier' health service.

(a) Firstly, while GP fundholders are able to shop around to buy the best services for their patients, the patients of non-fundholders are restricted to where their GP's Health Board or Authority has placed its contracts.

(b) Secondly, hospitals which are desperate for money rely on the revenue from GP fundholders and, as a result, the patients of fundholders are able to jump the queue at the expense of those who may have a greater clinical need.

(c) Thirdly, the fundholding scheme has widened standards within general practice by allowing only fundholding GPs to use their savings to improve their services.

2 GP fundholders have an incentive to manage their patients on the basis of cost rather than on that of medical need. This has destroyed the traditional doctor-patient relationship of trust in the following ways. Firstly, if a GP chooses to restrict treatment by, for example, not referring a patient to hospital or not prescribing drugs, the patient may start to wonder whether the deciding factor was financial rather than clinical. More worrying have been reports that some GP fundholders are refusing to accept, and are even striking off their lists, high-cost patients such as the elderly, poor and chronically sick.

3 Fundholding is an expensive way of organising the purchasing of services. Each fundholding practice receives up to £17,500 in preparatory costs when they enter into the system and an annual management allowance of up to £35,000 (1995 prices). The *Fundholding* magazine, however, estimated that when the knock-on costs, such as having to contract and bill for individual patients, are added up, the total expense comes to £81,638 a year for each practice. None of this money can be used to buy equipment for treating patients. Some observers, including the Audit Commission, have expressed concerns that the semi-independent status of GP fundholders has made national and local planning more difficult.

SELF-GOVERNING TRUSTS

Arguments For

1 Trusts have their own Boards of Directors who are able to make management decisions at the local level. It follows that, rather than waiting weeks or even months for a more remote Health Board to respond, Trusts now have power and control over the way they operate and this enables them to react faster to patients' needs.

2 Trusts have to compete with other providers in order to win and retain contracts and this has forced them to raise the standards of their service provision. Trusts have been helped in this task by the flexibility given to them to pay staff for additional duties. This has allowed them to make their services more convenient for patients by, for example, offering X-ray clinics in the evenings and operations at weekends.

3 Since 1991, Trusts have had the freedom to determine their own conditions of service and pay rates for all new employees and also for existing staff whom they have been able to persuade to abandon national terms in favour of Trust contracts. Moreover, in 1995 the pay review body announced that nurses were to receive a 1% national pay rise which could be supplemented by a further increase of up to 2% through local negotiations. Since local wage rises are dependent on how well the Trust is doing, the move in this direction means that staff now have a much stronger incentive than before to work towards improving the performance of their organisation. This can only benefit the NHS as a whole.

4 The efficiency and effectiveness of Trusts has enabled them to provide benefits for patients in two major ways. Firstly, between 1990 and 1993 there was a 16% increase in hospital activity levels (ie. the number of patient treatments), and in that period Trust hospitals outperformed non-Trust hospitals. Secondly, there have been marked improvements in those having to wait a long time for operations such as hip and knee replacements and cateracts. Indeed, the increased productivity of Trusts has enabled the government to improve on its original commitment in the Patient's Charter, so that now no patient will have to wait longer than 18 months for an operation.

5 Trusts have helped the NHS to make significant financial savings. Since Trusts no longer have to deal through the Health Board or Authority, a level of bureaucracy has been dispensed with and this has allowed management costs to be reduced. Furthermore, the requirement to draw up contracts with purchasers of health care has brought financial disciplines to bear on management and health care professionals by making them more aware of the costs of their clinical decisions.

Arguments Against

1 The introduction of Trusts has made the planning of an integrated health service more difficult. For example, in the past expensive items such as CT scanners were purchased by Health Boards/Authorities and placed in particular hospitals with the aim of serving the needs of the whole area. Now, however, Trusts are responsible for providing their own services and the fear of being disadvantaged in the competitive market system has meant that high-technology machinery, such as CT scanners is on all their shopping lists. This has resulted in the duplication and oversupply of certain services.

2 In the past, health service staff were encouraged to share information with others working in the NHS. With the splitting up of the NHS into separate Trusts, however, this information is now being closely guarded by the different institutions. Writing in December 1994, Dr Richard Smith, editor of the *British Medical Journal,* stated, "Speaking up on deficiencies within a hospital was once a public duty; now it is viewed as a betrayal of the competitive interest of the NHS Trust. Gagging clauses have been written into the contracts of NHS consultants and other employees...".

3 The move towards local staff negotiations will fragment the NHS into 450 separate units, each with the freedom to offer staff different pay and conditions. Those Trusts which are in a position to offer the best terms will be able to attract well-qualified and experienced staff, while others will become 'ghetto' hospitals. In this way, the NHS will cease to be a truly *national* health service.

4 Claims that increases in hospital activity levels and falls in waiting lists show that Trusts are successful should be viewed with caution. Firstly, with regard to hospital activity, the increase in the number of patients being treated is part of a long-term trend and cannot, therefore, be attributed to the reforms. Moreover, the government does not collect data on the number of patients treated, but on the number of patient treatments. This difference in terminology is significant for it means that if a patient is discharged from hospital too soon and then, as a result, requires further hospital treatment, he or she will be counted as another patient. In other words, the increase in hospital activity levels may be due to the inefficiency rather than the success of Trusts.

Secondly, while the longest waiting times have come down, this has been at the expense of an increase in shorter waits and the total number on waiting lists in England alone in early 1995 was over 1 million and rising. Furthermore, the reduction in the longest waits has had more to do with government funding earmarked for this purpose than with any increased efficiency on the part of the Trusts.

5 Between 1990 and 1994 the cost of simply setting up Trusts as self-governing units amounted to more than £120 million. This money, which was spent on things such as publicity, management consultancy and conveyancing fees, could have paid for an extra 6,000 nurses or 3,000 hospital consultants. In addition, a number of Trust hospitals have reported running out of money at the end of each financial year and have, as a result, been forced to delay admissions and postpone operations.

CONCLUSION

The jury then, is still out on the success of the reforms and on whether, in seeking a short-term remedy to some of its problems, they have merely succeeded in eliminating the strengths of the old NHS. Indeed, when a verdict is finally arrived at, the determining factor is likely to be the effect the reforms have had on the underlying principles of the NHS. On this question, two conflicting viewpoints have been put forward.

The first backs up the optimistic claims of the government that the disciplines of business and the marketplace have helped to tackle a number of the NHS's long-standing weaknesses by limiting the cost of health services, increasing productivity and delivering higher quality health care which is more responsive to the needs of consumers. As a result, it is claimed that both effectiveness and fairness have been achieved by the reforms and this has helped to strengthen the universal and comprehensive principles of the NHS.

The other viewpoint is pessimistic, believing that the introduction of market principles and competition into the NHS has produced a system which is inherently unequal in the way it delivers treatment and care and, as a result, has created a 'two-tier' health service. It is claimed, for example, that GP Fundholders are able to 'buy the best', that their patients can 'queue jump' at hospitals which are forced to rely on their custom, that patients who live in areas where purchasers 'buy well' do better than those who do not and that some hospitals have emerged as 'winners' at the expense of others which have 'lost out'. Consequently, the quality of care has been eroded, consumer choice has been limited and, most seriously of all, the principles of equality of access and treatment based on need have been sacrificed.

For the moment, opponents of the government's reforms have no alternative other than to work with the new system. In the run-up to the next general election, however, there can be little doubt that the debate will gather momentum and this will ensure that health care will once again be at the very centre of the political agenda.

Chapter FIVE

Going Private?

THE ISSUE of privatisation in the health services has, arguably, provoked more heated debate than any other. It is also true to say that it is an issue which causes a great deal of confusion. Even the Royal Commission on the National Health Service, which reported in 1979, admitted that defining 'private practice' or 'private health care' is a difficult task. Part of the problem is that the term 'privatisation' can cover a number of quite different practices within the area of health care.

Perhaps its most common usage is when it describes the practice of patients 'going private' and paying for the services of GPs, hospital doctors or hospital provision. It is sometimes also used to describe imposing charges for health care services, such as drugs, appliances, dentures and spectacles. To complicate matters even further, three relatively recent developments have also been defined as aspects of privatisation. Firstly, the term is now often used to describe the practice of the public sector buying services from, or contracting services out to, the private sector. Secondly, some have claimed that the operation of the 'internal market', with NHS Trusts and private providers competing for the business of Health Boards/Authorities and GP Fundholders, is another dimension of privatisation. Finally, it has also been used to describe the growing number of joint ventures which are taking place between the public and private health care sectors.

All of these definitions of the term 'privatisation' create their own issues and controversies. In any discussion over privatisation, therefore, it is essential that the meaning with which the term is being used is clearly defined.

THE TRADITION OF PRIVATE HEALTH CARE

Although the debate over the respective merits of public and private health care has deepened in recent years, private medicine is not, of course, a new development. By the 19th century, private medical schemes were available to the wealthy and to working men. With the introduction of the NHS in 1948, though, it was assumed that, as the benefits of the 'free' public system became immediately apparent, the reasons for people seeking private medicine would become irrelevant. Even then, however, the Labour government conceded the right for public and private medical care to coexist.

While this public-private mix has always existed in the health care arena, the NHS, as Bevan had hoped, quickly earned the overwhelming support of the British people. As a result, few consumers chose to opt for private health care and the virtual monopoly of the NHS as the comprehensive provider of free health care seemed assured.

The number of people insured for private health care did, however, grow slowly but steadily in the first twenty five years or so of the NHS's existence. Private practice became concentrated in particular specialist fields, mainly surgical and medical and some short-term psychiatric care. It became more prevalent in the affluent Southeast of England. Although the treatment of private patients relied heavily on NHS pay beds, the number of pay beds in NHS hospitals actually fell from just over 7,000 in 1956 to only 4,500 in 1974.

The narrow base of the private sector within the NHS did not mean, however, that the issue was completely free from controversy. Indeed, private practice always had its fair share of critics, particu-

larly among those who believed that it had harmful effects on the public sector. It was argued that not only were pay beds in NHS hospitals heavily subsidised out of the public purse, but also that keeping pay beds empty for potential private patients created growing waiting lists for NHS patients.

Thus, the claim went, the increase in the number of people insuring themselves for private health care had resulted in the creation of a two-tier health system.

When the Labour Party won the General Election in February 1974, its manifesto included a commitment to "phase out private practice from the hospital service". Following the *NHS Services Act* of 1976, one thousand pay beds were immediately abolished from the NHS and the Health Services Board was established to phase out the rest and to regulate the development of the private hospital sector. By 1979 the number of NHS pay beds had been reduced to about 2,800. Mainly as a result of the uncertainty over the future of private beds within the NHS, the private sector began to build new hospitals to cater for their customers. It is, therefore, somewhat ironic that by threatening private practice within the NHS, the Labour government contributed to the growth of the private sector.

SUPPORT FOR PRIVATISATION

There was fairly widespread support within the Conservative government elected in 1979 for the concept of privatisation. There may have been differing views on the ideal public-private mix in health care, but all were agreed that the existing, predominantly public, provision was inefficient and failed to satisfy consumer demand. The private sector, on the other hand, was viewed as being better managed, more efficient and more responsive to consumer choice.

Despite its ideological commitment to the free market, however, Mrs Thatcher's government was unable to carry out the logic of its rhetoric by abolishing the NHS—or at least reducing its role to that of a 'safety net' for the poor—and replacing it with a system based on private provision. It had to recognise that, in a situation where every measure of public opinion suggested continuing and overwhelming support for the principles of the NHS, the implementation of such radical proposals would carry quite unacceptable political costs. Indeed, this appreciation of the political realities forced Mrs Thatcher to reassure voters periodically that the NHS was "safe" in Conservative hands.

During the 1980s and 1990s, however, the Conservatives were returned to office for second, third and fourth terms on a platform of "rolling back the state", curbing public expenditure and encouraging private enterprise and market values. While they might have been unwilling to privatise the NHS outright, as they had done with most other nationalised industries, they were able to encourage the private health care sector actively through a number of measures which some people claimed amounted to no more than a policy of 'creeping privatisation'.

A summary of these measures is shown in the box

Creeping Privatisation

1 The Health Services Board, which had been set up by the Labour government to preside over the phasing out of pay beds and to control the development of private hospitals, was abolished in 1980.

2 The contracts of full-time consultants working within the NHS were modified in 1980 to allow them, for the first time, to engage in private work.

3 In 1981 employers were allowed to set health insurance premiums against corporation tax, and tax relief on health insurance as a fringe benefit was introduced for employees earning less than £8,500 per year. In 1989 tax relief on private health insurance was extended to those aged over 60.

4 Health Boards and Authorities were instructed to put certain services (catering, cleaning and laundry, for example) out for competitive tendering.

5 There were large increases in prescription charges and for all forms of dental treatment and new charges were introduced for sight and dental checks.

6 The change outlined in the *NHS and Community Care Act 1990* blurred the distinction between the NHS and private sector providers. For example:

a) Health Boards and Authorities and Fundholding GPs are now allowed to purchase treatment for their patients from the private as well as the public sector.

b) Trusts are now expected to operate in much the same way as private hospitals by selling their services in the marketplace. There has, as a result, been a big increase in the number of separate private pay bed units within Trust hospitals.

7 In 1992 the government introduced the *Private Finance Initiative* which was aimed at persuading the private sector to invest in capital developments in the NHS.

Charges vary from hospital to hospital, but the following is a rough guide to the cost of selected operations (1995 prices).

Tonsillectomy	£670–£1,650
Hernia Operation	£1,100–£2,200
Appendectomy	£1,500–£3,200
Hysterectomy	£3,000–£4,000
Hip Replacement	£5,200–£7,200
Heart Operation	£3,800–£8,300

Table 5.1
Source: Various

entitled 'Creeping Privatisation'. The impact of these policies can best be judged by examining five areas of activity: private health insurance; private acute hospital provision; cooperation between the public and private sectors; competitive tendering; and privatisation in primary care.

PRIVATE HEALTH INSURANCE

Those who seek private health treatment can, if they have the means, pay for it out of their own pockets. As you can see from table 5.1, however, private treatment is not cheap—and it could end up costing even more if complications arose and the patient had to stay in hospital for longer than was anticipated. Not surprisingly then, about 90 per cent of private patients pay their bills through private medical insurance schemes.

Origins and Development

The private medical insurance market has its origins in the 'non profit making' Provident Associations which were established earlier this century to cover the medical bills of their members. The creation of the NHS, and with it the right of every individual to obtain free medical care, threatened the very existence of these Associations. Although their business fell away sharply in the period immediately after 1948, in the mid-1950s it began to pick up again. This can be attributed partly to the increasing prosperity enjoyed by the growing middle class, but it seems unlikely that the private health sector would have benefited from this had it not been for the financial constraints placed on the NHS and the growing concern and dissatisfaction with the services which it provided.

Private medical insurance continued to grow slowly but steadily throughout the 1960s and early 1970s, although it dipped slightly in the period 1975–77 when the Labour government's phasing out of pay beds undermined public confidence in the ability of medical insurers to deliver the private health care they promised. As it turned out, though, this was to be a mere temporary blip.

Take-Off

When the Conservatives were returned to office in 1979, around 4 per cent of the UK population were covered by private health insurance. Following the election, however, the numbers began to soar; in 1980 they rose by over 27 per cent and in 1981 by 15 per cent. Such spectacular growth as this led to Dr Gerard Vaughan, the Minister for Health, predicting that by the mid-1980s 25 per cent of the population would be covered by private insurance.

This proved to be far too optimistic a claim. There was a steady growth in the insurance market throughout the 1980s but, in the early 1990s subscriptions began to fall for the first time since the mid-1970s. Although the number paying for their own medical insurance continued to rise, this increase was more than wiped out by the effect of recession-hit companies buying less cover for their employees. Nevertheless, the rate of expansion of private health insurance since 1979 has been impressive and by 1994 approximately 13 per

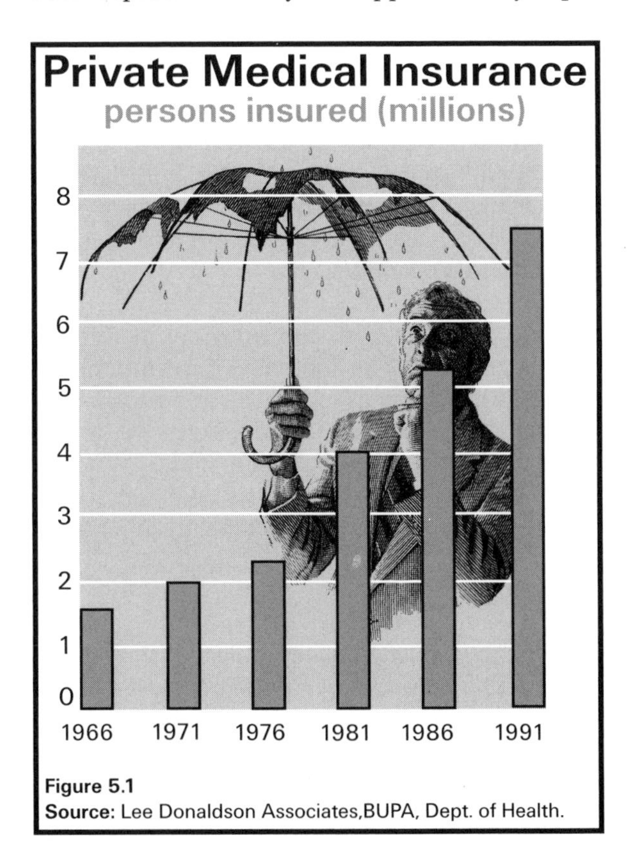

Figure 5.1
Source: Lee Donaldson Associates,BUPA, Dept. of Health.

cent of the population were insured against the costs of medical treatment.

Tax Relief

The most direct way in which Conservative governments have attempted to provide a boost for the private health insurance market has been through the introduction of tax relief. In 1981 two measures which intended to help expand the number of employees covered by health insurance were announced, but it was the decision to extend tax relief to the over-60s age group from April 1990 which created the most controversy.

Health insurance providers had been lobbying for such a measure for a long time. They had recognised that not many over-60s took out private insurance and yet there was a growing market in terms of both numbers and affluence. The private medical insurers, therefore, were quick to welcome the government's proposals, and responded by offering various schemes to meet the new tax relief rules.

The problem for the insurers, however, is that the older people get, the more prone to illness they tend to become, and so the more it costs to insure them. Thus, even with basic tax relief of 24 per cent, the cost of premiums for this age group is still high. Another disincentive for the over-60s is that personal health insurance cover is virtually confined to acute short-term ailments curable by surgery, whereas the elderly are often more in need of long-term care for conditions such as arthritis.

Not surprisingly, therefore, the scheme has not been taken up very widely. It has proved to be very expensive to administer though, and in 1994 it cost the Treasury £95 million in lost revenue. This led some commentators to claim that the government had put its ideological commitment to promote the interests of the private sector before those of the NHS and the taxpayer.

The Providers

The private health insurance market is dominated by two Provident Associations, BUPA (British United Provident Association) and PPP (Private Patients Plan), who between them have almost 75 per cent of the market share. These Provident Associations have 'non-profit' status, but this does not mean, as many people believe, that they are charitable organisations. Just like other insurance companies, they are run along strictly commercial lines and they have subsidiaries which are unashamedly 'for profit' organisations.

With a market estimated at the value of £1.5 billion in 1995, it is hardly surprising that new operators, for example general insurance companies such as Norwich Union and Municipal and General, began to enter the field.

EXCLUSIONS in most policies

- ✗ All ailments known to exist before starting the policy
- ✗ Services of a GP, dentist or optician
- ✗ Health checks
- ✗ Long-term hospital or nursing care
- ✗ Transplants
- ✗ Treatment on a kidney machine
- ✗ Fertility treatment
- ✗ Pregnancy and childbirth except, in some cases, when there are complications
- ✗ Vasectomy and sterilisation
- ✗ Abortion, unless medically necessary
- ✗ HIV and AIDS-related conditions
- ✗ Cosmetic surgery, unless necessary after an accident
- ✗ Suicide attempts and resulting injuries
- ✗ Illnesses caused by alcohol or drug abuse
- ✗ Homeopathic or other alternative medicine
- ✗ Appliances such as wheelchairs
- ✗ Any treatment not referred by a GP

Types of Policy

Private medical insurance can be obtained in two ways: individuals can pay for their own personal insurance or subscriptions can be paid through workplace-based 'group' schemes. The majority of group schemes are wholly paid for by the employer and are offered to the employee as a perk, just like company cars. Others are 'assisted' schemes, which are paid for partly by the employer and

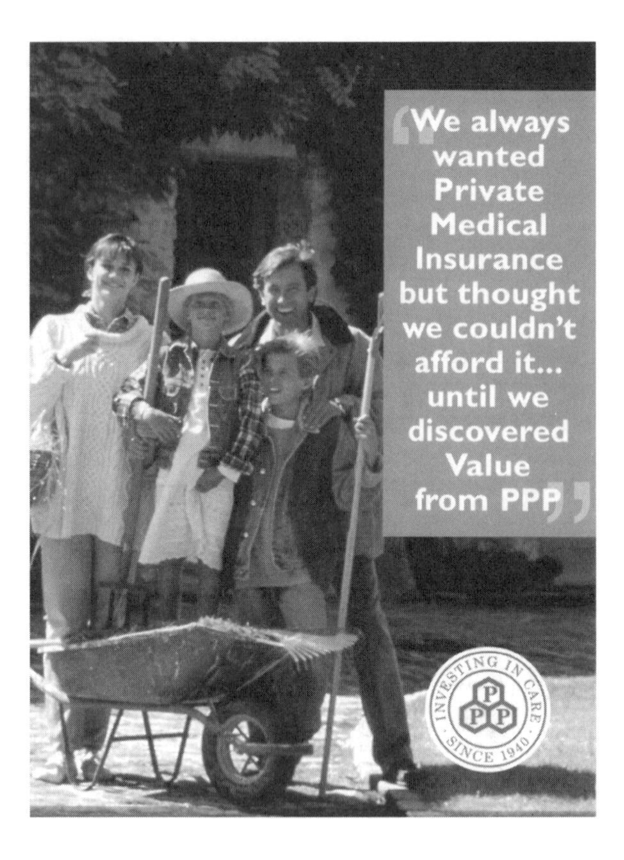

partly by the employee. A third type is paid for wholly by the employee, although they still benefit from the discounts (of anything up to 40 per cent) enjoyed through the terms of group membership.

The most rapid area of growth in medical insurance has been that of the company-paid schemes which in 1993 accounted for nearly 60 per cent of all policies, compared to 40 per cent in 1977.

The growing popularity of private medical care, along with the increasing competition between the Provident Associations and the commercial companies, has meant that prospective customers can now choose from a wider range of health care packages than ever before. These packages can be broadly classified into three categories: top-of-the-range, standard and budget policies. Top-of-the-range plans give full cover for treatment in most or all private hospitals and usually include extras such as home nursing. Standard plans cover a more limited range of hospitals and have fewer extras. Budget plans offer an even narrower range of hospitals and often cover a limited range of illnesses and restrict private treatment to when the waiting times for NHS treatment is longer than six weeks.

All private schemes, however, even the top-of-the-range ones, contain certain exemptions (see box entitled 'Exclusions in Most Policies'). Costs vary enormously between the three categories of plan. For example, in 1995 a single adult aged 30 would have paid about £300 per year for a budget policy and about £1,300 per year for a top-of-the-range policy. As mentioned earlier, premiums also vary according to age. A single person aged 60, for example, could expect to pay double or even treble the premium paid by a single 30-year-old for the same policy.

Disparities in Cover

For commercial reasons, private insurers are not keen to release statistics on the characteristics of people who have opted for private health insurance. On the evidence which is available, however, it is clear that there are wide variations in such cover in terms of age, social class and regional location.

a As we have seen, the cost of health insurance increases significantly the older a person gets. Although people aged 60 or over qualify for basic rate tax relief, premiums for the over-65 age group remain the most expensive of all. Indeed, people who suffer from poor health—a condition more prevalent among the elderly—can even be refused cover altogether. A further difficulty is that when people retire they lose any benefits they might have had from discounts through their employer's group scheme. Not surprisingly, therefore, the proportion of the 65–74 age group covered by health insurance is about half that of those aged under 65.

b Partly as a consequence of the high cost of health insurance and the growing importance of company-paid schemes, the majority of customers enjoying such cover come from high income groups. The most recent statistics—which relate to 1987, the last year in which the General Household Survey asked about private health care—show that while 27 per cent of professionals and 23 per cent of employers/managers had some medical insurance cover, this compared with only 2 per cent for the semi-skilled and 1 per cent for the unskilled groups.

c The General Household Survey showed that in 1987 there were also large regional variations. The Southeast of England had the highest coverage (parts of Buckinghamshire had rates in excess of 20 per cent) and the North of the country the least (Scotland had only about 4 per cent). This may, in part, reflect the higher standard of living and greater concentration of private health care facilities in the Southeast of England.

It might also, however, be a consequence of different social and political attitudes, as survey results consistently suggest that in the North the majority of the population support the idea of collectivism, or state welfare, while in the Southeast there is a more general acceptance of individualism, or private welfare.

PRIVATE HOSPITALS

When we talk about 'private hospitals' what exactly do we mean? Unfortunately, there is no simple answer, for the words hospital, clinic and nursing home are often used interchangeably. For our purposes here, however, the definition will be limited to those private institutions which concentrate on medicine and surgery, and which are roughly comparable to NHS services. The private sector's residential homes for long-term care will be examined in Chapter 7.

Small Beginnings

As we saw earlier, Bevan accepted the continuation of pay beds within NHS hospitals after 1948. The principal reason for this was to buy off opposition from the consultants, but he also saw it as a device which, he hoped, would help to curb the development of private hospitals and nursing homes. He was proved to be correct, for in the period following the creation of the NHS, demand for private medical care collapsed, and the majority of the small number of patients who continued to receive private treatment did so within the NHS pay bed system.

The Provident Associations became concerned by the lack of provision of private hospital beds outside the NHS. As a result, BUPA established Nuffield Hospitals in 1957 with the aim of providing a chain of private hospital facilities throughout the country. Although the demand for private treatment was growing, it remained small and by 1973 there were still only 21 Nuffield Hospitals providing a total of a mere 668 beds.

Labour's attack on the whole concept of pay beds within the NHS in the mid-1970s unwittingly helped to stimulate the private sector. Fearing that NHS facilities might eventually be completely denied to them, the private sector embarked on an ambitious programme to expand the number of private hospital beds outwith the NHS.

Commercialisation

The rapid increase in demand for private health insurance which followed the election of the Thatcher government in 1979 provided further impetus for the private hospital sector. In particular, the new private hospital building programme was given a boost with the government's decision to abolish the Health Services Board and the resultant scrapping of development controls.

There was no tradition of commercial 'for profit' health provision in the UK and this provided an opportunity for foreign companies to enter the scene. US-owned commercial companies, in particular American Medical International (AMI) and Hospital Corporation of America (HCA), were initially very active in the British market and between 1979 and 1988 they managed to increase their share from 5 per cent to 22 per cent.

The religious and charitable private hospitals found it increasingly difficult to compete in this new commercial market and many went out of business. Although it continued to sponsor Nuffield Hospitals, BUPA decided to fight back against the foreign invasion by setting up its own 'for profit' organisation, BUPA Hospitals Ltd. The US companies, however, were experiencing financial problems in their own domestic market and in 1989 HCA sold their British facilities to BUPA Hospitals and the French company Compagnie Général de Santé acquired the British hospitals of AMI.

As you can see from the box 'Trends in the Private Hospital Sector', there has been a transformation in the provision and ownership of the private hospital sector since 1979. In particular, there has been a rapid growth in the number of private hospital beds, the commercial 'for profit' sector has managed to increase substantially its share of the market and foreign corporations have taken the opportunity to make a significant contribution as independent acute hospital providers.

Trends in the Private Hospital Sector

1 In 1993 there were 11,416 beds in independent acute hospitals, compared to 6,671 in 1991.

2 In 1994 nearly 19 per cent of all UK hospital-based health care was provided by private and voluntary hospitals and nursing homes, compared to just over 7 per cent in 1984.

3 In 1993 commercial hospitals accounted for nearly 65 per cent of all beds in private hospitals, compared to under 30 per cent in 1979.

4 With the departure of the US hospital chains, European groups (eg. from France, Germany and Switzerland) increased their activity and by 1993 they accounted for 16 per cent of all private beds in the UK.

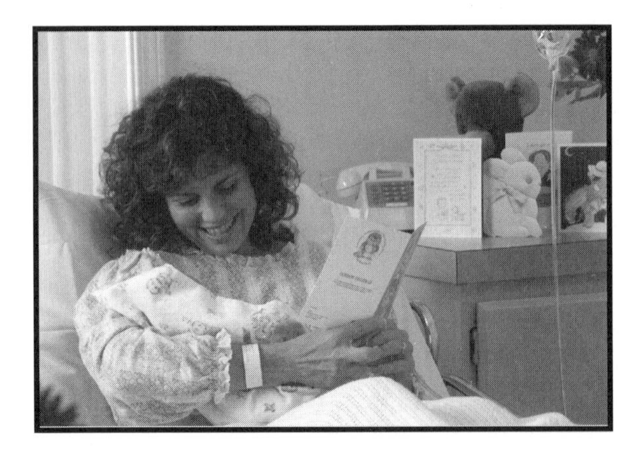

The Threat from NHS Pay Beds

Pay beds have existed within the NHS since it was set up in 1948. As mentioned earlier, however, the number of NHS pay beds went into decline even before they were drastically reduced by the 1974–79 Labour government. Although the incoming Conservative government abolished the Health Services Board, and with it the commitment to phase out pay beds, the hospital building programme by the private sector was by then well under way and the use of NHS pay beds fell even further during the 1980s.

The creation of self-governing Trust hospitals, however, has sparked a revival in the use of NHS pay beds. Trusts have been encouraged to generate business by looking for opportunities to sell their services in the marketplace and, as a result, they have begun to view pay beds as a potential money spinner. While private treatment in NHS pay beds was worth £65 million in 1986, this had increased to an estimated £215 million in 1994. Consequently, the NHS's share of the private acute care market grew from just over 10 per cent in 1990 to about 15 per cent in 1994. The private hospital sector has watched this development with alarm. It has complained of unfair competition claiming the NHS uses public money to subsidise private patients and this enables it to undercut the prices of private hospitals. Research funded by Norwich Union in 1995, however, found that, while there was some evidence of Trusts not accounting for all costs (such as administration and heating) in their prices, even if these were included, their economies of scale would still allow them to undercut private hospitals considerably.

Extending Services

Traditionally, the bulk of the private sector's clinical activity has been confined to non-emergency routine elective surgery. One way in which the private hospital sector has attempted to fight back against the growing competition from the NHS has been to look at ways of extending its range of services. For example, many private hospitals and clinics now offer specialised health screening units which are designed for the early detection of diseases such as heart disorders, high blood pressure, breast and cervical cancer.

The private hospital groups and health insurers have also set up occupational health services to provide companies with information and guidance about how their employees' health may be affected by conditions at work. Some private hospitals and clinics have begun to provide short-term psychiatric care for alcoholics, drug addicts and those suffering from nervous disorders. Others have diversified into areas such as kidney dialysis centres and maternity services. Private hospital companies have also been looking at ways of extending collaboration with the public sector as a way of helping to protect their business.

PUBLIC-PRIVATE PARTNERSHIPS

Collaboration between the public and private sectors is not new. What became different in more recent times, however, was the extent to which this relationship developed, much of it as a direct result of government policy.

Joint Ventures

In the past, joint ventures between the two sectors were usually confined to high-technology projects. For example, PPP contributed financially to help maintain the heart transplant programmes at Harefield and Papworth Hospitals and BUPA helped St Thomas' Hospital in London to buy a lithotripter (a machine which destroys kidney stones by the use of sound waves instead of surgery). On the other hand, private hospitals often hired equipment from the NHS. For example, when Mrs Thatcher went into a private hospital in 1983 to have an eye operation, it was done with equipment hired from the local NHS hospital.

In recent years, there has been a significant growth in the number and type of partnerships between the private and public sectors. Health Boards and Authorities were instructed by the government to make use of private facilities as part of the drive to reduce waiting lists. More controversially, the government introduced the Private Finance Initiative in 1992 with the aim of persuading the private sector to finance, build and even manage new hospitals or departments. In 1993 the limit on private funding without Treasury approval for capital projects within the NHS was raised from £250,000 to £10 million. By 1995 some 40 projects worth more than £100 million had been approved.

The Internal Market

The contract system introduced with the health service market changes in 1991 allowed private providers to compete on an even basis with NHS

The Public v Private Health Care Debate

Arguments against private health care

1 In the NHS all patients should be treated equally and according to need. Private medicine, on the other hand, is based on the ability to pay. It has created a two-tier health system—one (private medicine) for the well-off who seek care for acute conditions, and one (NHS) for the poor and the chronically and seriously ill.

2 Hospital consultants who are engaged in private work have a vested interest in keeping waiting lists long. Surveys repeatedly tell us that growing NHS waiting lists is one of the main reasons for people turning to private medicine. No private company would tolerate its senior staff investing in, and working for (often using the company's equipment) what is, in effect, a rival business. However, this is what is happening in the NHS.

3 When people choose to go private they are, in practice, queue jumping. Private hospitals deal with the easy work, leaving the difficult and expensive complaints to the NHS. The NHS does not charge economic rates for its pay beds. As a result, it is subsidising its private patients.

4 The majority of nurses working in the private sector were trained in the NHS at public expense. Moreover, many of them have special skills, such as intensive care and operating theatre skills, which are in short supply in the NHS.

5 Evidence suggests that some consultants who work for both sectors tend to neglect their public patients and favour their private ones. Private work interferes with NHS efficiency.

6 Most private hospitals do not have on-site emergency facilities and if a crisis develops private patients have to be treated by the NHS. Private patients often find that the cost of their treatment is far higher than they had been led to believe.

7 Many private patients are articulate and influential members of society. If they used the NHS for routine treatment, they would be unlikely to accept low standards or long waiting lists, and they would insist on improvements to the service. Private medicine is concentrated in areas such as the Southeast which already have good NHS facilities. Thus it exaggerates inequalities in health provision.

8 Foreign profit-making companies are becoming an important interest group and may well be able to influence a change in direction for British medicine and health policy.

Arguments for private health care

1 Private treatment is not a luxury which only rich people can afford. Patients in the independent sector now represent a cross section of society through group insurance schemes. For example, union deals have brought firefighters and police officers into private health group insurance schemes.

2 Long NHS waiting lists mean that many patients are faced with an anxious and often painful wait of many months, or even years, before gaining admission. In the private sector, patients can get immediate admission for non life-threatening operations. In the private sector, patients can choose the consultant who is to carry out their operation, and they enjoy extras such as individual rooms with telephones, colour TV, en suite bathrooms and a wide choice of food.

3 Pressure is taken away from the NHS when people turn to private medicine. Since private hospitals concentrate on 'cold surgery', NHS waiting lists for these non-urgent cases are reduced, leaving the NHS to deal with emergencies and chronic complaints. The NHS receives much-needed additional income from private patients who use pay beds.

4 A number of private hospitals offer courses in basic nurse training and post-qualification specialist training. This can also benefit the NHS as these nurses can leave the private sector at any time to work for the NHS.

5 Private practice enables hospital consultants to receive earnings similar to those they could earn abroad. This helps to stop a 'brain drain' of our hospital consultants.

6 Private hospital and insurance companies have donated pieces of equipment to NHS hospitals, to be used by both public and private patients. Some types of treatment, for example cosmetic surgery, are only available in the private sector.

7 The existence of the private sector means that the Exchequer has to spend less money on health care. Also, private patients still contribute to the running of the NHS through their compulsory national insurance contributions. When people spend their money on private medicine they are helping to add to the total amount of resources spent on health care.

8 The private sector has attracted foreign capital into the country and so is a valuable export earner.

providers for the business of Health Boards and Authorities and GP Fundholders. Official figures show that the amount of taxpayers' money spent on private treatment for health service patients rose from £215 million in 1991/92 to £388 million in 1993/94, representing a rise of 80 per cent in only two years. Despite this rate of increase, however, private hospital operators complained that with a total NHS budget of some £39 billion, they should have been receiving a lot more NHS work.

Private Practice by NHS Consultants

As we have seen, NHS consultants have been allowed to practice private medicine since the very outset of the service. In 1980 the government modified the contracts of full-time NHS consultants to allow them to engage in private work provided they did not earn more than 10 per cent of their gross income from this source. Furthermore, consultants were able to opt for 'maximum part-time' NHS contracts under which they could forego one-eleventh of their salary in order to be free to earn unlimited income in the private sector. It has been estimated that about 85 per cent of NHS consultants are involved in private practice. Estimates of consultants' earnings from this private activity range from an annual average of £17,000 to an average of £40,000 on top of average NHS pay of £57,000 (1995 figures). Some London consultants, however, were thought to have been able to make over £200,000 per year from private work.

COMPETITIVE TENDERING

The term 'competitive tendering' refers to the process whereby an organisation invites competition for certain services between the existing work force (known as the 'in-house' work force) and the private sector. All interested parties are invited to put in bids which outline the services they would provide in terms of both quality and cost and, in theory at least, the bid which offers the best value for money is given the contract.

The Conservative government elected into office in 1979 was committed to the idea of the privatisation of public services. As you can see from the box entitled 'Preparing the Ground', the government initiated several steps which were aimed at easing a move towards competitive tendering in the NHS. It was following the government's re-election in 1983, however, that a circular was issued instructing all Health Authorities to put out their ancillary services (catering, cleansing and laundry) to competitive tender. Health Boards in Scotland were encouraged to do the same, but unlike their English counterparts, there was no compulsion to comply and few services in Scotland were put out to tender. The Scottish Health Boards, however, were brought back into line with the rest of the country following the elevation of Michael Forsyth, a Thatcher loyalist and long-time supporter of competitive tendering, to the position of Scottish Health Minister in 1987.

Preparing the Ground

1 Before the Conservatives came to power, Health Boards and Authorities paid no Value Added Tax (VAT) on services which they provided for themselves, but did pay VAT on any services they bought from private companies. The government changed this, however, by providing for an automatic refund of VAT for services placed with outside organisations.

2 The government repealed the Fair Wages Resolution. This meant that private contractors could pay their staff lower wages than 'in-house' staff whose wage rates had been agreed nationally.

3 The government methodically changed the composition of Health Board and Authority membership. Many members apathetic or hostile to the Conservatives' objectives were replaced by enthusiastic supporters.

4 Health Boards and Authorities were instructed to cut their staffing levels. Since staff employed by private companies were not included in NHS staffing totals this, in effect, was a direct encouragement for competitive tendering.

The Competitive Tendering Experience

At the outset, many private firms were desperate to gain a foothold in what they saw as a lucrative market. Thus, many of them submitted artificially low, or 'loss leading' bids which they intended to offset against the larger and more profitable contracts which, they hoped, they would then be in a position to win. Not surprisingly, the 'in-house' teams found themselves unable to compete with these bids and by 1984 the private companies were winning 74 per cent of all NHS contracts. By 1985, however, the share of all contracts won by private companies had been reduced to just over 50 per cent and by 1990 to only 23 per cent. Some of the reasons to help explain this disappointing trend for the private sector are shown in the box entitled 'Barriers to Private Sector Involvement'. In the early 1990s, however, the numbers began to pick up again and by 1993 about one in three contracts were held by the private sector. There have been wide variations in how the contracts for ancillary services have been awarded. Firstly, in terms of the sectors of the service, private contractors have won about 30 per cent of cleaning contracts, about one-quarter of laundry contracts and a mere 8 per cent of catering contracts. Secondly, in terms of geography, private firms have been most successful in the Southeast of England, particularly in the areas which lie just outside London.

One effect of the diminishing share of contracts being won by the private sector has been to encourage the process of mergers and takeovers. It has enabled a small number of large multinational companies to dominate the private market within the health service. For example, by 1990 two firms had cornered 66 per cent of all private cleaning contracts; three companies held 74 per cent of all private laundry contracts; and three firms had won 81 per cent of all private catering contracts.

Extending Service Coverage

Despite the somewhat disappointing record of the private sector, the Conservative government remained politically committed to pursuing its policy of competitive tendering. Consequently, Health Boards and Authorities were pressurised into finding new ways of encouraging the private sector to increase its share of business within the NHS. The response was the identification of new target areas.

(i) The government's White Paper *Working for Patients* suggested that a wider range of services should be offered for competitive tendering. As a result, services which went out for tender were extended to include portering, security, computing, medical records, pharmacy, laboratory and non-emergency ambulance services. More recently, emergency ambulance services have been added to the list and in 1995 Department of Health guidelines made it clear that private companies could also provide clinical services, such as renal dialysis, if outside tenders were lower than 'in-house' bids.

(ii) Health Boards and Authorities were encouraged to put out 'multi-service contracts' to tender. This involved combining a whole range of services, for example catering, cleaning, portering and security, within one highly lucrative contract. Some companies found these contracts attractive since not only did this allow them to extend their business base by involving them in a range of new services, it also enabled them to use their staff flexibly by moving workers from one type of a job to another.

(iii) The *NHS and Community Care Act* separated the purchaser and provider roles within the health service. In order to satisfy this requirement it was expected that Health Boards and Authorities would shed many of their functions. As a result, several of them set up 'trading agencies'—organisations separate from Health Boards and Authorities, with their own directors and accounts and whose funding depends entirely on their ability to generate their own income. Others allowed management buy-outs of services such as estate management and pathology.

Barriers to Private Sector Involvement

1 Some private companies found that they did not have the necessary experience, skills or resources to meet the required specifications and, consequently, ceased to operate in the market.

2 Others discovered that they did not make the expected profits out of their new ventures and decided against retendering.

3 Some Health Boards and Authorities were forced to bring services back 'in-house'. This was due to private contractors failing to meet specifications or abruptly pulling out altogether.

4 The organised resistance of health workers locally and political opposition from some Health Boards and Authorities discouraged many private companies from retendering or, indeed, tendering in the first place.

The Case in Favour of Competitive Tendering

(i) The government's principal argument was that it would produce substantial savings for the NHS. Unlike the NHS, health services in other countries, such as the United States, placed a far heavier reliance on outside contractors. It was this practice which, it was claimed, enabled these countries to spend much less on their ancillary services than was the case in the UK. By 1992 it was estimated that competitive tendering had achieved savings in direct costs to the NHS of about £150 million per year.

(ii) Any savings made on these ancillary services can be reallocated to areas which will be of more direct benefit to patient care. For example, in a document published in 1982, Michael Forsyth suggested that a 10 per cent saving in "hotel and general budget could support, each year, the purchase of 52,500 kidney machines, or 490 whole body scanners, or 51,000 extra nurses, or 17,600 extra doctors...".

(iii) The competitive tendering exercise forces administrators to draw up specifications for contracts put out to tender. This means they have to work out performance indicators which specify what the service should be trying to achieve in terms of standards. Thus, the exercise helps to improve the quality of the services provided.

(iv) The Conservatives were elected on a manifesto pledging to weaken trade union power. Competitive tendering was viewed as an ideal method for helping to achieve this aim. If more services were provided by private companies, the work force would be smaller, more flexible and less unionised. It has been estimated that in the first ten years of competitive tendering approximately 30,000 ancillary workers were made redundant and there had been a marked increase in the use of part-time staff. Moreover, the majority of private contractors involved in the NHS do not recognise trade unions. As a result, there has been much less industrial action in the NHS since competitive tendering began.

(v) The Conservatives were also convinced of the merits of the 'free market'. They believed that market principles would deliver more efficient services, but even if the cost-cutting aspects of competitive tendering reduced standards, as its critics claimed, then so be it. In the eyes of true 'free marketeers' this would have the beneficial effect of undermining the status of the NHS and thus persuading more people to choose the private sector for their medical care.

The Case Against Competitive Tendering

(i) Doubts have been expressed about the claim that competitive tendering has produced great savings. It is said that figures quoted by the government ignore additional costs involved in the programme. These include:

- The costs of setting up the programme, such as preparing specifications, advertising and evaluating bids.
- Running costs. If a contract fails, additional costs are incurred. At the very least, it involves extra monitoring to get the service back to the required standard. At worst, the tendering process will have to be started all over again.
- The costs of displaced staff. Tens of thousands of ancillary workers have lost their jobs and many more have lost earnings. Thus, there have been costs in terms of redundancy pay and in unemployment and other benefits. Social costs, such as poverty and illness caused by loss of earnings should also be added to the total bill.

(ii) Traditionally, the 'in-house' domestic staff were regarded as part of the multi-disciplinary 'ward team'. Most of the ancillary staff felt a commitment to the NHS and, particularly in specialities like geriatrics and mental health, they were expected to contribute to the general welfare of patients. They often took a liberal view of what their duties entailed and took over some of the simple caring tasks from over-stretched nurses. Competitive tendering, however, with its requirements of defining tasks and allocating staff on the principle of maximising profit margins, has destroyed the concept of the 'ward team'.

(iii) It is cost rather than quality considerations which determine whether or not a bid is successful. To produce the lowest bids, both private firms and 'in-house' teams have had to make cuts in staff and in hours. It is claimed that falling standards for patients has been the result.

The Public Services Privatisation Unit estimated that in 1992 about 5 per cent of privately-run contracts in the NHS had been terminated due to inadequate standards.

(iv) Whether it be private firms or 'in-house' teams who win contracts, the results are the same: redundancies, reduction of hours, pay cuts, increased productivity, worsening conditions and higher staff turnover. As a result, there has been a serious deterioration in morale among staff, who are predominantly female and poorly paid. Moreover, the traditional rights of staff to have their grievances heard through trade unions and employment protection legislation has been denied to many.

(v) Tendering has failed to increase competition in the way that free marketeers had predicted.

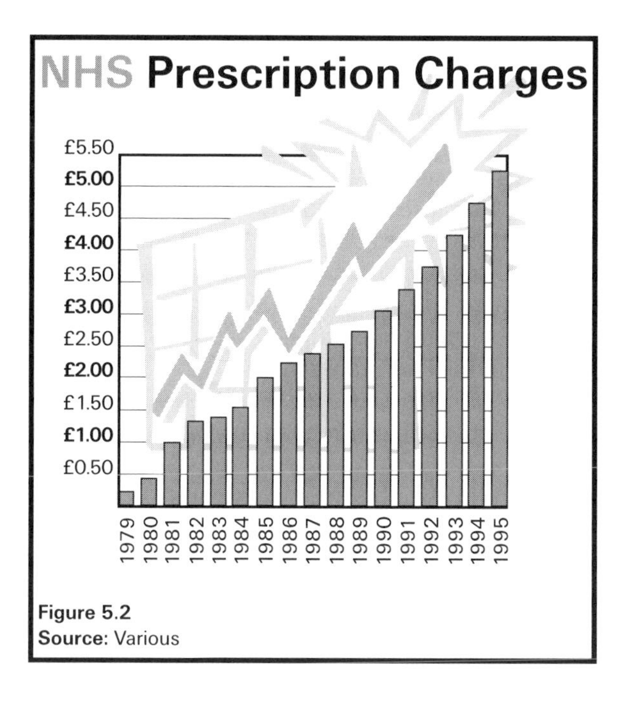

Figure 5.2
Source: Various

The majority of NHS contracts have been won by 'in-house' teams with the rest being concentrated in the hands of only a small number of private companies. Also, it is claimed that the commercial culture of the free market is inappropriate to a public service. For example, how can those involved in management buy-outs reconcile their commitment to the NHS with the contradictory incentive of making profits for their commercial business?

PRIVATISATION AND PRIMARY CARE

Discussions about expanding private health care, which at first were focused on the hospital sector, have now moved into the primary care arena. Although there are experiments under way with regard to privately-run and financed GP practices, privatisation in primary care has crept forward on two main fronts: first, by increasing charges and, second, by adopting a market solution in the area of optical services.

Dental Services

When the NHS was set up, all dental treatment was free. It did not last long though, for in 1951 dentures, along with spectacles, were the first health service items to be subjected to charges. Since then, but particularly since 1979, dental charges have risen substantially.

In 1979 patients paid the full cost of dental care up to £5, after which all treatment was free; by 1995 patients had to pay 80 per cent of the full cost up to a maximum of £300. In future, patients may have to pay the full NHS fee for complicated treatment if a government proposal made in 1994 is taken up. Also, free dental check-ups were abolished in 1989. Free NHS dental treatment is now available to certain exempt people: children, pregnant women, nursing mothers, and those on income support or family credit.

A bitter dispute developed between the government and the dental profession following a decision in 1992 to cut by 7 per cent the fees which dentists received from the state for providing NHS treatment. The two main unions, the British Dental Association and the General Dental Practitioners Association, responded by urging their members to refuse to take on any new NHS patients.

Not all dentists complied with this call, but between 1992 and 1995, nearly 900,000 NHS patients were de-registered as more and more dental practices began to look for private customers.

A survey carried out by the Consumers Association found that 64 per cent of people had their dental care wholly or partly paid for by the NHS in 1995 compared with 80 per cent in 1992. The choice for many patients, therefore, had become one of either paying private fees (anything between twice and four times the NHS rates) or taking out a policy with one of the insurance companies such as Denplan or BUPA. It also provoked accusations that the Conservatives' real intention was to privatise NHS dentistry.

Optical Services

Over the years a number of actions have been taken with regard to optical services. Firstly, charges for NHS spectacles were increased, then the supply of subsidised spectacles was limited to children and those on social security before being withdrawn altogether. Now everyone needing spectacles has to buy them privately, although children and the poor continue to get help with the cost in the form of vouchers. Secondly, the opticians' monopoly in the dispensing of optical prescriptions was broken and commercial organisations were given the right to produce glasses according to an optician's prescription. Thirdly, free sight tests were done away with and replaced with a £10 charge (although children, students up to the age of 19, people on income support, the partially sighted and those suffering from diseases related to blindness were exempt).

Prescriptions

There is no such thing as a popular tax, but prescription charges must rank as one of the most loathed of them all. As you, can see from figure 5.2, however, the Conservatives were not slow to impose increases on what some people called this 'tax on the sick'. When the Conservatives took office in 1979, NHS prescription charges stood at 20p per item, while by 1995 they were 26 times higher at £5.25. (If the increase had kept pace with inflation it would have risen to only 53p.) People on repeat prescriptions can buy a pre-payment certificate which entitles them to free prescriptions, but charges for these have also risen and in 1995 they cost £27.20 for a four month certificate and £74.80 for an annual certificate.

As with dental and optical charges, not all people have to pay for their prescriptions. Indeed, over half of the population is exempt from prescription charges—children, pregnant women and nursing mothers, those on low incomes, people suffering from certain medical conditions and pensioners. Mainly due to the elderly receiving an average 13 prescriptions a year compared with eight for the rest of the population, about 80 per cent of all prescribed items are dispensed free. A House of Commons health select committee report in 1994 called for a major shake-up in the system. It recommended a lower charge for prescriptions but that fewer prescriptions be issued. Others have argued for the scrapping of charges altogether, believing that the cost should be met fully from taxation. At the time of writing, however, there was no indication that the government was considering either of these options and further increases in charges seemed the most likely future scenario.

The government has defended its policy on increased charges in a number of ways. It claimed, for example, that faced with a spiralling drugs bill (£3.3 billion in 1995), increased charges were essential both for finding additional means of funding and for limiting demand for medicines. Also, exemptions meant that the less well-off and most needy in our society were protected from these charges. Finally, the whole notion of charges was consistent with the Conservatives' belief in the principle that individuals should take responsibility for their own health.On the other hand, critics argued that charges had an adverse effect on NHS patients. The Royal Pharmaceutical Society expressed concerns that people on low incomes but who fall just outside the exemption category, or those on multiple medication may forego all or part of the prescription.

As a result, the patient may need a second visit to his or her GP, or, if the untreated condition deteriorates, costly hospital treatment. The British Dental Association claimed there was strong evidence that people were going for longer between visits and ending up requiring more repair work. More worryingly, serious illnesses such as oral cancer might go undetected. According to the Association of Optometrists, there was a 30 per cent reduction in the number of eye tests following the introduction of charges. Moreover, it was claimed that these charges were inconsistent with the government's own emphasis on preventing illness. More generally, it was argued that one of the founding principles of the NHS—that an inability to pay would not bar people from treatment—has been seriously weakened.

PRIVATISATION AND THE FUTURE

Compared to most other countries, the private health sector in the UK remains relatively small. Even so, whichever indicator of privatisation is considered— whether it be the proportion of people insured, the number of private treatments, the privatisation of services or increased levels of charges —its growth in recent years has been significant. This expansion can partly be explained by the existence of persistently long waiting lists and continuing concerns about the quality of NHS care, and partly by the policies of Conservative governments which, since 1979, have been ideologically committed to the promotion of the private sector.

Perhaps the most important development in recent times has been the blurring of boundaries between private and public health care. The *NHS and Community Care Act* has enabled private providers to compete on an equal basis with NHS providers for the business of the purchasers of health care. While this has afforded opportunities for the private sector, it has also presented them with difficulties. Trust hospitals are increasingly using their new freedom to operate in the commercial market by developing their own private en suite rooms and the fact that they have on-site emergency facilities and can offer cheaper prices has given them a competitive edge over private hospitals. The private sector has proved itself to be extremely resilient, however. Bevan's assumption that the setting up of a free and comprehensive public health system would result in the withering away of the private sector was clearly wide of the mark. The expansion of private health care since 1979 has created a powerful political lobby in its favour which any government—whatever its ideological persuasion—will certainly be forced to take account of.

Chapter SIX

Inequalities in Health

ONE OF the fundamental principles on which the NHS was based in 1948 was a commitment to remove inequalities in the provision of health care. The NHS established the principles of collective responsibility and equal access to medical attention regardless of the financial, social or cultural position of the individual. Since 1948 the percentage of Gross National Product (GNP) being taken up with health care expenditure has risen dramatically. Medical advances have resulted in great improvements in the quality of care available. The standard of living of most people has grown steadily which has made it easier for people to secure the necessities for a healthy lifestyle. It is not unreasonable to assume, then, that inequalities in health care would have disappeared long ago.

In practice, however, the situation has been quite different. As we have seen, the growth of private medicine and the introduction of competition through the internal market has led some people to claim that we have now gone back to a two-tier medical care system. However, even before these developments,there was mounting evidence that certain groups of the population were experiencing inequalities in health. A person's financial resources, social position, ethnic origin, sex and the area in which they stayed seemed to affect their chances of achieving good health. More recent research seems to suggest that, if anything, these inequalities are deepening.

HEALTH AND ILLNESS

Any attempt to assess variations in health standards between different groups of the population must begin with an analysis of health and illness trends. Before doing even that, though, we need to be clear about what health actually is.

What Is Meant By Health?

The answer to this question may seem obvious. Nevertheless, it is an issue which has caused much debate and is one which has important implications for the direction of health policy. There are two alternative interpretations of what is meant by health.

1 *The Medical Model:* This view defines health in somewhat narrow and negative terms as simply the absence of illness and disease. The emphasis of this approach is gaining better health through curing illness and disease rather than through preventive measures. The medical model has a long tradition, starting with herbal remedies and attempts at primitive surgery, and continuing with the high-technology medicine of the present day.

2 *The Social Model:* This is a more positive interpretation, which defines health, in the words of the World Health Organisation, as a "state of complete physical, mental and social well-being and not merely the absence of disease or infirmity" (WHO 1946). The social model then, takes on a more comprehensive approach. While recognising that medical advances are important for good health, it emphasises that attention must also be directed to wider issues, such as prevention of disease and illness and to gaining more knowledge about the social causes of ill health and death.

There are a number of difficulties associated with both of these interpretations. For example, those who adhere to the medical model would label as 'healthy' people who we might wish to classify as 'unhealthy'—such as those who, although free from disease and illness, are suffering from the effects of poverty. On the other hand, supporters of the social model as defined by WHO would regard as 'unhealthy' people whom we might prefer to label as 'healthy'—such as seriously disabled people who are nevertheless able to lead full and contented lives.

Of the two interpretations it is the medical model which has tended to carry weight with the bulk of resources being diverted into the short-term, or acute, sectors of medicine and with those who work in these areas being given the higher status.

How do we Measure Health and Ill Health?

Since there are different ways of defining health, problems arise when we try to find suitable statistical indicators to help us to measure it. As the medical model tends to be the one normally used, the most common methods employed to measure the health status of populations are negative ones, ie. mortality (death) and morbidity (disease and sickness).

Mortality: These statistics are the most readily

AGE ADJUSTED MORTALITY RATES: BY SELECTED CAUSE AND SEX, 1992 (RATE PER 100,000 POPULATION)

	Heart Disease	Respiratory Diseases	Cancer	Road Traffic Accidents	Suicides and Open Verdicts
Males					
England	309	116	296	11	17
Wales	334	115	301	11	21
Scotland	382	146	334	13	23
NI	377	185	289	13	14
Females					
England	251	116	260	5	6
Wales	261	115	263	4	6
Scotland	311	155	286	5	8
NI	306	209	254	7	3

Table 6.1
Source: Adapted from *Regional Trends* 29 (1994), Table 7.7.

available and are the most reliable. Death is an undisputed event which legally is required to be registered. These records are useful for the purposes of planning services when they show *what* people die of, the *rate* of 'premature' deaths (especially infant deaths), and *variations* between different social classes, occupations, gender and ethnic groups, or regions of the country. Mortality figures also have their limitations though, since they do not tell us anything about the level of illness in a community or about the quality of life.

Morbidity: This data, which measures all forms of ill health, is a potentially more valuable guide to the population's wellbeing. Statistics on sickness and disease, however, are much harder to come by. They can be worked out from the records of hospital in-patients, GP consultation rates and data on absence from work. These are generally regarded as invalid measures since not all sickness and disease comes to the attention of doctors and not all absence from work is due to illness. The census provides statistics on sickness, but these are only available every ten years and cannot be analysed by age or class. The main source of information is the *General Household Survey* of some 15,000 households, which is carried out every year. The major drawback with this, as with the census figures, is that the data relies on individuals reporting *themselves* as having health problems. Thus, the accuracy of this data is clearly open to question.

Despite their limitations, mortality and morbidity data continue to be our main measurements of health. The problems they pose, however, should be borne in mind when studying the statistics in the pages which follow.

HEALTH SERVICE STAFF (1991)

(rate per 10,000 population)

England	176.2
Wales	208.6
Scotland	241.2
NI	242.7

Table 6.3
Source: Adapted from *Regional Trends* 29 (1994), Table 7.21.

GEOGRAPHICAL INEQUALITIES

North-South Divide

Much of the recent debate about inequalities in health has concentrated on the differences in ill health experienced by people in different regions of the country. In 1987, the Health Education Council stated, "From 1979–83 data, death rates were highest in Scotland, followed by the North and Northwest regions of England and were lowest in the Southeast of England and East Anglia, confirming the long-established North-South gradient". More recent information on mortality and morbidity rates would seem to confirm these findings and this is illustrated in table 6.1 above.

HEALTH AUTHORITIES EXPENDITURE, 1990–91

£ per head

	Administration	Hospital Services	Community Health	Other Expenditure	Total Expenditure
England	16.03	230.36	41.23	50.46	338.08
Wales	16.54	260.09	42.51	54.10	373.24
Scotland	20.93	337.11	38.88	59.75	451.67
NI	29.30	308.06	42.48	52.69	432.53

Table 6.2
Source: Adapted from *Regional Trends* 28 (1993), Table 6.12.

There are similar variations throughout the country in the distribution of both health care expenditure and health service employees. This is clearly illustrated in tables 6.2 and 6.3. As you can see, however, these figures show little correlation with the data on mortality and morbidity (table 6.1). Indeed, Northern Ireland and Scotland (the areas which experience most ill health) have expenditure per head considerably above that for England (which enjoys much better health) and also employ more staff in relation to the population served.

Of course such variations in the allocation of financial and manpower resources are, in large part, a reflection of these different areas having different needs, and take into account such factors as patterns of ill health, degree of deprivation, and distribution and age structure of the population.

Resource Allocation

In 1970 Julian Tudor Hart, a GP working in a poor area in Wales, pointed out that health care provision tended to be worse in areas where health needs were greatest. He called this "an inverse care law" and explained that "in areas with most sickness and death, general practitioners have more work, larger lists, much less hospital support ... than in the healthiest areas; and hospital doctors shoulder heavier caseloads with less staff and equipment, more obsolete buildings and suffer recurrent crises in the availability of beds and replacement staff."

In an attempt to tackle this issue, the government in 1976 set up a 'Resource Allocation Working Party' (RAWP) in England and a group to look into 'Scottish Health Authorities Revenue Equalisation' (SHARE) north of the border. Their tasks were to develop a formula which would allow a more equal distribution of funds between different geographical areas in the two countries by weighting allocations with regard to the needs of the population.

The RAWP and SHARE approaches did make some progress although tight government restrictions on NHS spending meant that regional inequalities were never totally eradicated.

The principles worked out by the RAWP and SHARE groups formed the basis for allocating resources to Health Boards and Authorities up until the introduction of the internal market which, as we have seen, encouraged the notion that money should follow patients to wherever treatment was on offer.

Whether market forces will help to bring about a fairer allocation of resources or, as some claim, merely heighten the impact of the 'inverse care law' is as yet unclear.

Local Differences

Recent research in this area, however, has indicated that basing policies solely on the principle of tackling geographical inequalities is much too simplistic an approach. There are areas in Scotland and Northern Ireland, for instance, which compare favourably with the healthiest areas in the Southeast of England, while there are parts of London which have records of poor health comparable to the most deprived areas in the country. Indeed, as you can see from the newspaper article, '*The area where poverty and poor health walk hand in hand*', there can be wide variations in health within a radius of less than one mile in one city. The problem, then, is not just one of a North-South divide. As one commentator has remarked, "there is a national problem with regional overtones rather than a regional problem requiring isolated action." (*Health and Deprivation; Inequality and the North.* Townsend et al). As a result of this, researchers have now directed their attention towards social class as an explanation for the unequal distribution of health.

SOCIAL CLASS INEQUALITIES

The Black Report

The link between social class and health was strengthened in 1980 with the publication of a report called *Inequalities in Health.* The report was the product of a research working group chaired by Sir Douglas Black, President of the Royal College of Physicians and former chief scientist at the DHSS. The inquiry had been commissioned by the Labour government three years earlier but the report, which has generally come to be known as the *Black Report,* was handed over to a Conservative administration.

The new Conservative government showed little enthusiasm for the *Black Report.* In the rather short foreword to the report, which was written by the Secretary of State for Social Services, Patrick Jenkin, it was suggested that the research had not shown the factors responsible for health inequalities, and that many of its recommendations were unrealistic. Only 263 duplicated copies were made available at a cost of £8 each, and the usual practice of holding a press conference and issuing a press release was not observed. The medical journal, the *Lancet,* came to the not surprising conclusion that the government seemed to be "keen to reduce the report's impact to a minimum". If it was the government's intention to keep the contents of the *Black Report* secret, it did not succeed. The trade union COHSE and the Trade Un-

The area where poverty and poor health walk hand in hand

Two parts of Glasgow have provided new evidence that the poor face greater health risks than the rich, writes Bob Wylie

DRUMCHAPEL AND BEARSDEN, less than one mile apart as the crow flies across Glasgow, stand at a crossroads of socio-economic inequality in Europe.

Geographical twins on the north-western pages of a streetfinder atlas, they are separated by a huge gulf in health standards similar to the differences between Poland and Sweden, and offer hard evidence for the *British Medical Journal's* statement last week that poverty and bad health go hand in hand.

A young man celebrating his 21st birthday in Drumchapel this morning is two and a half times more likely to be dead before the age of 65 than his counterpart living two miles away in Bearsden.

Before they are 65, men in Drumchapel are three times more likely to die of heart disease or bronchitis than men in Bearsden.

They are two and a half times more likely to die of a stroke, and run double the risk of dying from lung cancer.

Death from heart disease, bronchitis, strokes and lung cancer similarly creates a chasm between the women of Drumchapel and those from Bearsden. In addition, women from Drumchapel are almost three times as likely to die from breast cancer. And once they are stricken with the disease their chances of survival are less. Five years after getting breast cancer 58% of women from Bearsden are still alive. Only 48% survive that time in Drumchapel. They are four times as likely to be admitted to a psychiatric hospital than their affluent neighbours too.

These new statistics are drawn from a report, completed last week, of a study by Greater Glasgow Health Board into Drumchapel and Easterhouse and the latest report of the city's director of public health published last year.

In the three-year period—1990–1992—when the Drumchapel data was collected there were a total of 163 deaths from the six major causes studied.

The GGHB report shows that if Drumchapel residents shared the same general health standards as Scotland as a whole then 71 of those who died would still be alive.

If they shared the same health as Bearsden residents then only 65 of the 163 would be dead.

Glasgow is following national trends identified in a series of studies linking death rates to wealth distribution; the more you have, the longer you have to enjoy it. This week the British Medical Association is convening an international conference, Action on Social Inequality and Health, in London.

The studies showed that after the deduction of taxes and benefits the incomes of the richest 20% in Britain were four times as large as the poorest 20% in 1981. By 1991 they were almost six times as large. This increasing gap in income levels between rich and poor is being matched by similar disparities in death rates, according to the BMJ.

Dr Richard Wilkinson, senior researcher at the University of Sussex, said: "Reducing the burden of excess mortality attributable to relative deprivation depends on reducing social and economic inequalities themselves." He said that the more deprived sections of the population have paid a heavy price for the official failure to take the social causes of disease seriously.

"If risks as great as these resulted from an exposure to toxic materials then offices would be closed down and people evacuated from contaminated areas."

Glasgow's director of public health, Harry Burns, said yesterday that the BMJ's conclusions were broadly in line with the GGHB's recent findings and its last public health report: "It is increasingly obvious that there are links between the psychological stress of poverty and unemployment and physical ill health."

He said that one of the BMJ papers which argued that serious physical illnesses such as cancer and heart disease may be caused by the stress of unemployment was clearly "an issue of great concern for Glasgow."

However, Burns cautioned against a 'knee-jerk' reaction to the GGHB and BMJ findings, which sought to tackle the problems with a demand for more spending in the NHS. "In a way this would be the equivalent of the captain of the Titanic calling for more buckets to bail out the water."

He said that GGHB was already targeting its health care resources to those most in need whilst accepting that this remained an exercise in "damage limitation".

If the findings of the studies were to be taken into account then investment in jobs, education,housing and training was the real answer to inequalities in health. "The best thing that could happen to Glasgow's health would be the arrival of new hi-tech factories to provide high value jobs for the people of Drumchapel, Easterhouse, Pollok and Castlemilk," said Burns.

Source: *Scotland on Sunday,* 5 May 1994.

ion Congress (TUC) both published summaries of the report for their members, and in 1982 the publishing company Penguin brought out a paperback version which allowed the report's evidence and arguments to reach a wide audience. Despite government rejection, the *Black Report* became the focus of much academic attention and sparked off a large number of pieces of research.

The Evidence

What did the *Black Report* say that the Conservative government found so difficult to accept? The report was the most thorough study ever carried out into how people in different social classes felt about their health or ill health. The Black Working Group studied health statistics by social class between 1921 and 1971. Although aware that it had its limitations, Black decided to use the same classification of social class as the previous studies he was reviewing. This was based on people's occupations, and on the Registrar General's categories which you can see in table 6.4. The problems of using occupational class in such studies are summarised in figure 6.1. The *Black Report* concluded that while the health of the nation had improved, inequalities in health had not been eliminated. On the contrary, the report argued that the evidence strongly suggested that the health gap between the higher and lower social classes was widening. The Working Group found that there were marked increases in the rates of both mortality and morbidity as you moved down from social class 1 to social class V. These class inequalities in health started in childhood and continued throughout life. The result, states the *Black Report,* is that "a child born to professional parents, if he or she is not socially mobile, can expect to spend over 5 years more as a living person than a child born to an unskilled manual household". Figure 6.1 shows the class inequalities at different stages of life. How these inequalities affect people in different social classes is illustrated in the extract from *The Unequal Health of the Nation:* A TUC Summary of the Black Report on page 57.

The Recommendations

The authors of the *Black Report* argued that the NHS needed policies to address these persistent class health inequalities. They also concluded, however, that these inequalities could be explained by the social and economic conditions experienced by different groups and that, as a result, the solution lay beyond the NHS. The report's remedy involved a number of wide-ranging recommendations for improvements in the NHS, personal social services, social security, housing and education. The main themes were:

1 There should be a major attack on poverty, directed especially at families with children and at disabled people. The report argued for a shift of resources towards community care within the NHS and also personal social services. Included in its proposals were an expanded programme of nursery facilities for the under-fives, the introduction of a comprehensive disablement allowance and additional resources for the elderly and the disabled to allow them to be cared for in their own homes rather than in residential institutions.

2 Much greater emphasis should be given to preventing ill health rather than to curing it. The government should commit itself to the introduction of effective preventive and educational action with the aim of encouraging changes "in people's diet, exercise and smoking and drinking behaviour". The report had a clear set of recommendations on smoking, including bans on advertising and sports sponsorship, a ban on smoking in public places and regular tax increases on tobacco, leading to the "eventual phasing out of sales of harmful tobacco products at home and abroad".

Where You Live Can Seriously Damage Your Health

1 Scotland, Northern Ireland and Wales have higher infant mortality rates than England.

2 Scotland has a higher death rate from cancers and strokes than other parts of the UK.

3 Scotland and Northern Ireland have higher rates of heart and circulatory disease than England and Wales

4 In England, health is worse in the North and Midlands than in the South.

5 There are areas in the North (eg. Bearsden in Glasgow) where the population's health is as good as anywhere in the country, while there are areas in the South (for example, Brixton in London) which have levels of health as poor as anywhere in the North.

3 The government should undertake a broad anti-poverty strategy with the aim of achieving a relative improvement in the living standards of poor people. As the report stated: "While the health care service can play a significant part in reducing inequalities in health, measures to reduce differences in material standards of living at work, in the home and in everyday social and community life are of even greater importance". The report, therefore, called for a radical programme including the redistribution of income, increased access to employment, improvements in working conditions and increased spending on public housing. A significant reduction in social inequalities in health, said Black, could only be achieved through such deep-rooted structural change.

Such an ambitious programme would, of course, cost a lot of money and the Social Services Secretary estimated that it would amount to £2 billion a year. It should come as no surprise, therefore, that the Conservative government, concerned as it was with containing public expenditure, should reject the recommendations of the *Black Report.*

Further Research

Since the publication of the *Black Report,* a number of major studies have been undertaken and their results have largely confirmed the findings of the original research. Whether the social

REGISTRAR GENERAL'S CLASSIFICATION

Social Class		Example of Occupations	Approximate %
I	Professional	Accountant, Doctor, Lawyer	5
II	Intermediate	Manager, Nurse, School Teacher	18
III	N. Skilled Non-Manual	Clerical Worker, Secretary, Shop Assistant	12
III	M. Skilled Manual	Bus Driver, Butcher, Carpenter	38
IV	Partly Skilled	Bartender, Postal Worker, Telephone Operator	18
V	Unskilled	Cleaner, Kitchen Hand, Labourer,	9

Table 6.4 **Note: Married women have traditionally been classified on the basis of their husband's occupation**

position was measured by occupational class, house or car ownership, level of education, or individual problems such as unemployment, the same picture emerged. The average life expectancy of the whole population is increasing, but these improvements are not being shared equally. Some of these studies are shown below.

1 Two distinguished researchers, Professor Raymond Illsley and Julian Le Grand, attempted to allow for the doubts expressed at occupation being the indicator of social class by putting forward an alternative method of calculating changes in health trends. Instead of looking at differences in mortality rates between social classes, they examined the age of death of people dying in different years. What they found was that, over the period 1921 to 1983, the number of people dying prematurely had fallen. As a result, the variation in the age of death of individuals in the population had narrowed.

This apparent decrease in inequality in the age of death has been used by some commentators as a

Objections to using Occupational Class as a Social Indicator in Studies of Health Trends

1 As soon as women marry, they are assumed to adopt the classification of their husband. This means that it is difficult to find out much about social differences among women.

2 Class composition changes over time. Between 1931 and 1971, for instance, membership of social classes I and II increased from 14% to 23%, while membership of social classes IV and V fell from 38% to 26%. Thus, the lower death rates in social classes I and II now apply to more people, and the higher death rates in social classes IV and V to less people. In other words, while the gap between the classes may be widening, the larger section of the population now belonging to social classes I and II might, in fact, indicate greater equality.

3 It only relates to people aged under 65. Most people are older than that when they die and health inequalities may not be so widespread in the older age group.

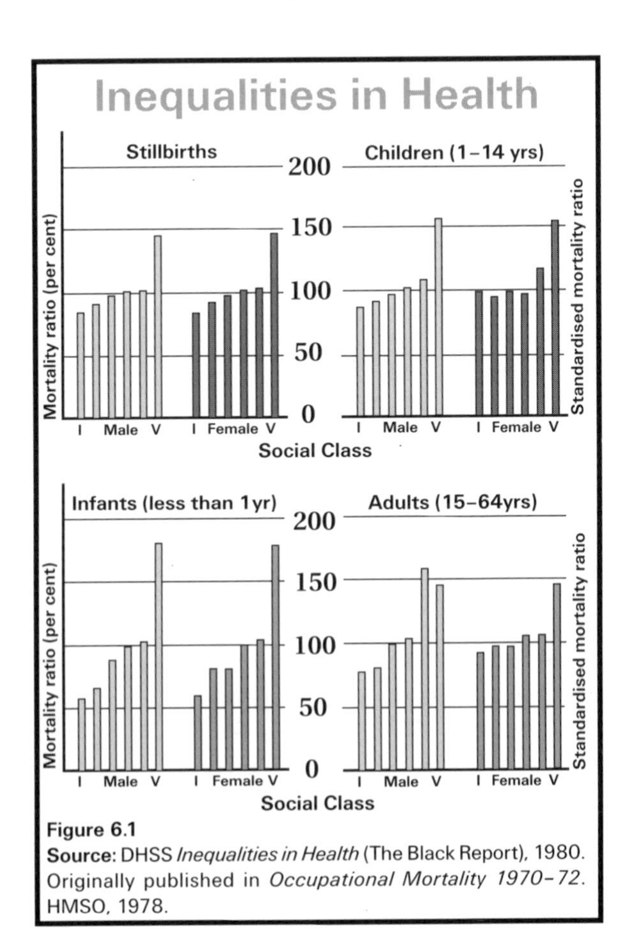

Figure 6.1
Source: DHSS *Inequalities in Health* (The Black Report), 1980. Originally published in *Occupational Mortality 1970–72*. HMSO, 1978.

reason for challenging the findings of the *Black Report*. However, the trends in the distribution of age at death which Illsley and Le Grand were looking at were not the same as the social differences which Black was measuring. This can be illustrated by examining changes in the causes of death. Since the 1920s, infectious and respiratory diseases, such as tuberculosis, have become rarer. Since these diseases caused high child mortality and mainly afflicted the poor, one would expect variation in the age of death to decrease. On the other hand, degenerative diseases, such as heart disease, have become more common. Although these diseases used to affect the rich more than the poor; the reverse is now true. However, the proportion of people dying prematurely from heart disease, under the methods of calculating changes used by Illsley and Le Grand, may not have changed at all. It, therefore is perfectly possible for the variations in the age of death of *individuals* to narrow while,

Health and Social Class

*According to the Black Report, health differences between classes and inequalities of life-chances can be traced through all stages of a person's life. This can be effectively illustrated if we take the case of two hypothetical families—the **Jones** and the **Smythes**.*

Mr Smythe is the financial director of a large company. **Mrs Smythe** does not work and she is soon to give birth to her third child. They live in a pleasant suburb on the edge of the green belt with their two children, **Emily** aged five, and **Rodney** aged 10. They own their own home and the area where they live is mainly populated by professional people. There are plenty of recreational and sporting facilities, good schools and a brand new health centre in the locality.

Mr Jones is an unskilled labourer at a factory. His wife supplements the family income by working as an office cleaner. They live in a high rise block of flats in the centre of the city. The flats were built in the late fifties and are poorly serviced with play areas and parks. The **Jones** also have two children, **Janet** aged five and **John** aged 10. **Mrs Jones** is expecting her third child. The family is registered with a local GP whose list of patients is already oversubscribed.

These two imaginary families are at opposite ends of the social scale in terms of occupation and income. In between there are different shades of grey, but how are these two different families likely to fare under the existing National Health Service arrangements? Based on the Black Report, these are some of the likely outcomes.

There is a 60% probability that **Mrs Jones** will not have consulted an obstetrician by the fifth month of her pregnancy. By that time it may be too late to diagnose congenital abnormalities like spina bifida or blood disorders in her unborn baby.

Mrs Jones's poorer living standards will probably mean her standard of nutritional diet is poor. She is nearly twice as likely as Mrs Smythe to die in childbirth, or her baby to be stillborn or die within the first few months of life. If her baby is a boy and survives birth, he is still four times more likely to die before his first birthday than Mrs Smythe's newborn son.

Like his brother **John**, the newborn Jones boy is ten times more likely to die before he is 14 through an accident involving fire, a fall or drowning than his counterpart Rodney Smythe. **John** is seven times more likely to be knocked down and killed in a road accident. Similar disadvantages will follow him to adult life. In only one case—asthma—is Rodney more likely to die than **John** at an early age.

Though statistics show that **Janet Jones** is not as likely to be an accident victim as her brother, her individual health and life expectancy will tend to follow the pattern of her mother and maternal grandmother.

Mr Jones's health and life expectancy is also considerably poorer than that of Mr Smythe—and if his son also becomes a manual worker his health is likely to follow a similar pattern too.

Although the actual health of all families has improved since the setting up of the NHS, the relative gap between professional and unskilled manual workers has actually widened.

Contrary to popular belief, **Mr Jones** is much more likely to die of lung cancer or duodenal ulcer than Mr Smythe. He is twice as likely to die of a disease affecting the nervous system; three times as likely to suffer and die from a parasitic disease; four times as likely to incur a mental disorder, or a respiratory disease, and die.

In contrast, the **Smythe** family are more likely to follow a nutritionally satisfactory diet, to consult preventive services such as dentists, chiropodists and opticians. **Mrs Smythe** is more likely to have planned her family than Mrs Jones, or to have been screened to test if she might have treatable breast or cervical cancer. The *Black Report* comments that health facilities tend to be geared towards the middle-class consumer rather than the working class.

Also the high-density urban areas where working-class people live tend to have a lower per capita expenditure than the suburban areas which are not so densely populated. The **Smythe** family are likely to have frequent medical check-ups as a matter of course —the **Jones** are more likely to use their GP after illness has set in, and consequently visit him more often.

*The unavoidable inference from the Black Report is that the people whose health is at greatest risk are those with the lowest incomes, and worst living conditions. Families like the **Jones** are the ones most at risk—they are also getting the worst deal out of the NHS.*

Source: *The Unequal Health of the Nation*: A TUC Summary of the Black Report *social inequalities* widen. Viewed in this way, the two studies are complementary rather than conflicting.

2 *The Health Divide*, published in 1987 by the Health Education Council, was an attempt to update and extend the findings of the *Black Report*. The press conference arranged to launch the new report was cancelled an hour before the start by the chair of the Health Education Council who said that the report was "political dynamite in an election year". Like the official reaction to the *Black Report* before it, the unintended result was to give the *Health Divide* greatly increased publicity.

The *Health Divide* found that "In 65 of 78 disease categories for men ... (the rates) for classes IV and V were higher than for either class I or II. Only one cause, malignant melanoma (skin cancer caused by over-exposure to the sun) showed the reverse trend". A similar situation existed for women with the research suggesting that "death rates among women from coronary heart disease and lung cancer actually rose in manual groups while showing a substantial decline in non-manual women".

Turning its attention from death rates (or mortality) to general health status (or morbidity), the authors of the *Health Divide* found the same trends. More recent information from the *General Household Survey* confirms these findings and indicates that the difference in illness rates between the classes becomes particularly noticeable in the 45–64 age group (see table 6.5). The conclusion of the *Health Divide* was that health inequalities had, in some respects, worsened since the publication of the *Black Report*. The main causes for this were put down to increases in homelessness, unemployment, income inequality and poverty during the 1980s.

3 A study published in 1988 called *Health and Deprivation: Inequality and the North* took a different approach by relating health status to four direct measures of material deprivation. It ranked electoral wards in terms of overall health (based on data on death rates, permanent sickness and disability) and related this to levels of deprivation (based on rates of unemployment, car ownership and overcrowding). It found that variations in health between local populations showed a close association with the four indicators of deprivation and that even "slight variations in social and economic well-being have parallels in slight variations in health".

4 In a major study in California it was found that the poorest group in the sample were one and a half more times more likely to die than the richest group, even after the data had been adjusted to take account of high-risk behaviour patterns such as smoking, drinking and lack of exercise. The study concluded that the evidence seemed to suggest that mortality rates of the poor were more likely to be affected by factors such as general living conditions and environment rather than by behaviour patterns.

5 In an important study commissioned by Barnardos and published in 1994, Dr Richard Wilkinson argued that it is not the "direct physiological impact" of poverty which damages our health but rather inequalities in the distribution of incomes. It was found that "standards of health in developed countries are powerfully affected by how equal or unequal people's incomes are". Also, it was argued "countries with the longest life expectancy are those with the smallest spread of incomes"—not the richest countries.

One of the implications of this study is that inequalities in health can perhaps best be tackled by measures which change the overall distribution of income and wealth rather than by attempts to merely reduce the worst aspects of poverty.

6 In 1995 a report called *Tackling Inequalities in Health: An Agenda For Action* was published by the independent health charity, the King's Fund. It showed that people from disadvantaged groups suffered from more disability and illness and died on average eight years earlier than people from affluent backgrounds.

While the report said that better access to health care should be provided, it argued that the contribution of the NHS to tackling health inequalities

Reported Ilness by Age and Social Class

Social Class	% of Males Reporting Long-Standing Illness at Age (Yrs) 0–15	16–44	45–64	65+
Professional	15	21	35	49
Employers, Managers	17	21	34	57
Intermediate Non-Manual	20	21	37	63
Junior Non-Manual	16	20	38	59
Skilled Manual	16	24	46	64
Semi-Skilled Manual	25	25	45	63
Unskilled Manual	13	28	55	66

Table 6.5
Source: *General Household Survey* 1992 (Published 1994), Adapted from Table 3.2.

could, at best, only be a modest one. Like the *Black Report*, it argued that what was required was radical changes to economic and social policies, such as the provision of better housing, the restructuring of the tax and benefit system and the creation of employment opportunities. As Sir Donald Acheson, the former chief medical officer for England and Wales who contributed to the report, said: "The existence of health inequalities... is indisputable. We hope that future debate will concentrate on constructive steps to improve the health of the less well-off."

What is to be Done?

There are two conflicting approaches to the explanation of social class inequalities and what the correct response to them should be in terms of health policy. One focuses on the individual while the other concentrates on much broader collective issues.

1 *Individualism*: This view explains class health inequalities in terms of differences in the way individuals in the various social groups choose to lead their lives. In this explanation, people in the various social classes behave differently in such things as the consumption of tobacco and alcohol, the types of food eaten, the type and amount of exercise taken and the use of preventive health services. It is argued that the adoption of such behaviour patterns and voluntary lifestyles within the social groups is the reason for inequalities in health.

There are, as figures 6.2, 6.3 and table 6.6 clearly demonstrate, significant differences in lifestyles between the social classes. There is also a substantial body of evidence linking smoking, heavy drinking, poor diet, lack of exercise and low uptake of preventive services with ill health. It would appear to be perfectly logical, then, to focus health policy on the individual with the aim of changing individual behaviour as a way of improving health and reducing social class inequalities.

This sort of view found favour with the Conservative government. As we have seen, by the mid-1980s it had been converted to the idea of allocating resources to a programme for preventive health education. One of the greatest champions in the government for this view was the former Junior Health Minister, Edwina Currie. She hit the newspaper headlines when she said that the real cause of the poorer health of Northerners was nothing to do with poverty but very often "is just ignorance", and that they should stop making themselves ill by smoking, drinking too much and eating too many crisps and chips.

2 *Collectivism*: According to this view it is economic and environmental factors, beyond the immediate control of the individual, which are responsible for social inequalities in health. People in the lower social groups are more likely to be exposed to health hazards at work and in the home. They also receive low wages or, in many cases, are forced to rely on near-subsistence level incomes from the state. This makes it much more difficult for them to afford the necessities for health, such as a nutritious diet and decent living conditions. Some researchers have suggested that inequalities in wealth (rather than poverty itself) may be another important factor. The collectivist approach was the one favoured by the *Black Report* and by most of the studies which followed it. The measures they recommended to tackle health inequalities all involved public intervention to reduce social and financial inequalities.

The debate over the merits of the individualist and collectivist approaches is an important one. For one thing, at a time when an increasing percentage of GNP is being swallowed up by health care expenditure, it is crucial that this money is spent

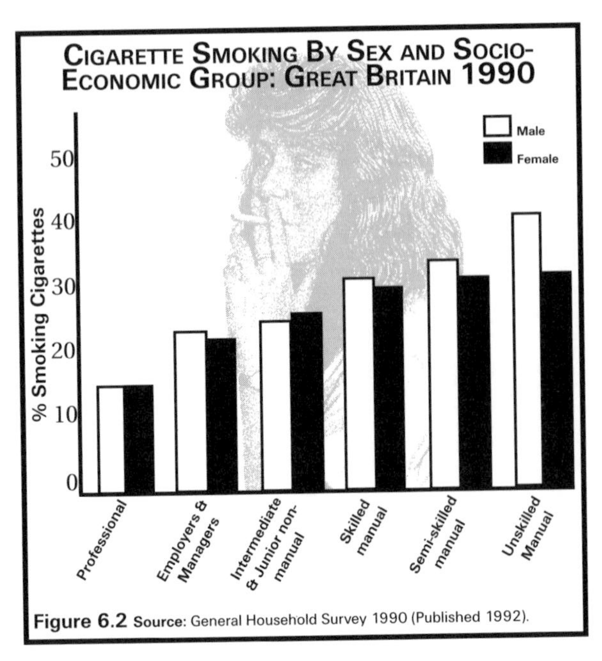

Figure 6.2 **Source:** General Household Survey 1990 (Published 1992).

wisely. More importantly, however, there is evidence to suggest that the gap between rich and poor is widening in the UK—in 1971 one in ten people earned less than half the national average income, but by 1994 this figure was one in five—which, in turn, means that it is likely that inequalities in health have also widened. As a result, it is even more essential that effective health policies to tackle inequalities are developed.

As we have seen, the response of the Conservative government was to commit resources to health education and prevention of disease in an attempt to change individual lifestyles and behaviour. Indeed, its 1992 *Health of the Nation* strategy dismissed out of hand the idea that social inequality played any role in causing illness (see Chapter 3). In 1994, however, it eventually did agree to set up a working party to examine "variations in health". Critics may have expressed disappointment about the rather limited scope of this inquiry, but they had to admit that this was at least the first acknowledgement from the government that factors such as income, unemployment and housing may have a bearing on the nation's health.

Whether it is also the first indication that the government is willing to move towards a broader agenda in tackling the problems of social inequalities in health remains to be seen.

GENDER INEQUALITIES

Although differences between the various social classes and regions of the country have been the areas of health inequalities which have received most attention, society is also divided in other ways. One of these is by sex.

Mortality Rates

As you can see from table 6.7, mortality rates have shown a gradual improvement throughout the twentieth century. The data also shows that in 1992 the life expectancy for a woman at birth was nearly five and a half years longer than for a man. In Britain in the nineteenth century (and in Developing Countries today), these sex differences in life expectancy were reversed. Since then, however, maternal mortality has declined and, as a result, women's life expectancy has increased. The figures suggest that while the gap in male-female life expectancy widened in the period from the be-

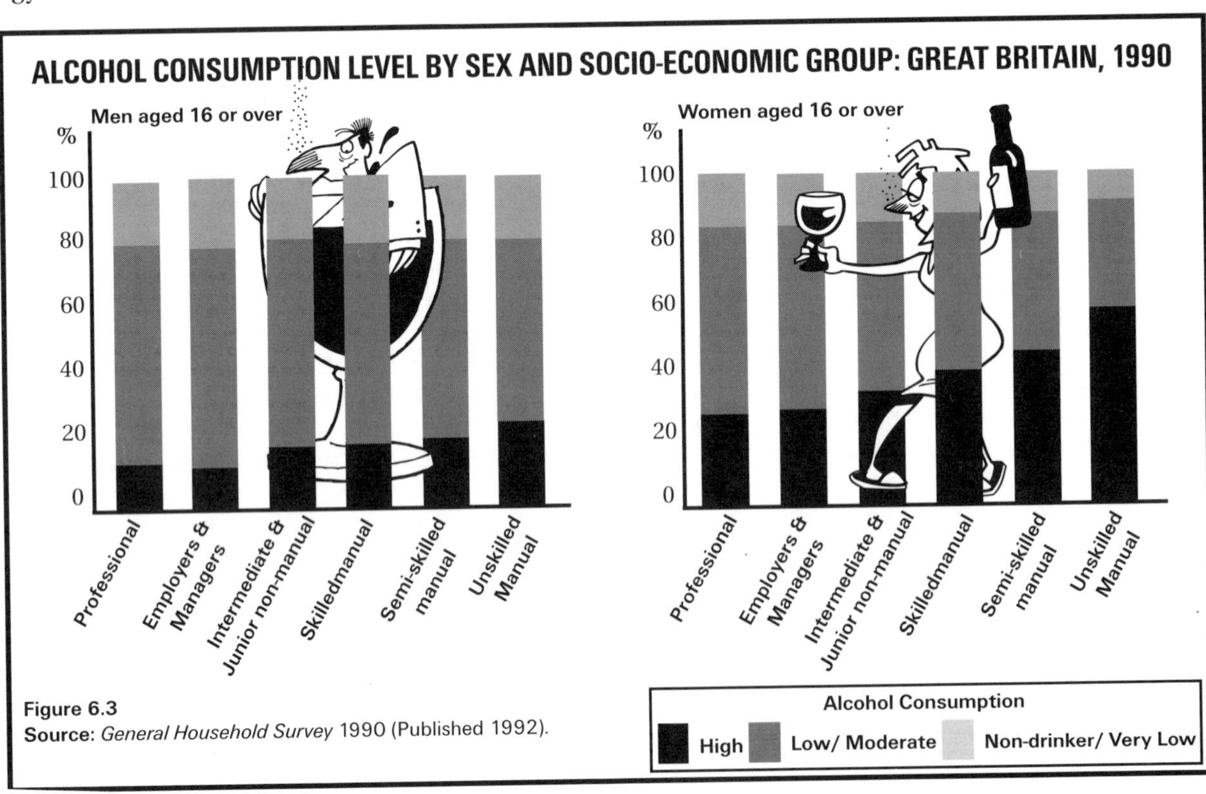

Figure 6.3
Source: *General Household Survey* 1990 (Published 1992).

Physical Activity Rates By Socio-Economic Group, 1990

	Professional	Employers and Managers	Intermediate & Junior non-manual	Skilled manual	Semi-skilled manual	Unskilled Manual
Walking	81	72	69	61	55	49
Swimming	63	50	48	37	31	22
Keep Fit/Yoga	18	17	28	9	16	10
Cycling	25	17	17	15	14	11
Golf	24	22	11	12	6	4
Jogging	18	12	9	8	5	3
Soccer	14	9	6	11	6	4
Badminton	14	9	10	5	4	2
Tennis	15	10	8	4	4	2
Squash	17	9	6	4	2	1
Bowls	7	7	5	6	4	4
Cricket	10	5	3	4	2	1
Skiing	11	5	3	2	1	0
Sailing	9	5	3	2	1	0
Climbing	6	3	3	2	1	1
Rugby	2	1	1	1	1	0

(Percentage participating in the 12 months before interview)

Table 6.6**Source**: *General Household Survey* 1990 (Published 1992)

ginning of the century to the 1980s, it has been reducing since then.

There are higher levels of male deaths in virtually every age group from birth right through to adulthood (see table 6.8). The causes of death, moreover, vary between men and women for different age groups. In the 1–14 age group, for instance, nearly twice as many boys as girls die from accidents and violence, while in middle age, deaths from lung cancer, heart disease, accidents and suicide are the major reasons for males' higher mortality rates.

Female mortality rates are higher than males for respiratory diseases (see table 6.1), while breast cancer and cancers of the genito-urinary system are major causes of death in women. Every year, breast cancer kills around 15,000 women in the UK, while cervical cancer claims a further 2,000.

As we saw in Chapter 3, screening programmes for both of these cancers were important aspects of the new GP Contract, and reducing deaths in women from these ailments were specifically targetted in both *Health of the Nation* and *Scotland's Health—a challenge to us all.*

Expectation of Life: By Gender, UK

Years

	1901	1931	1961	1981	1991	1992
Males (at birth)	45.5	57.7	67.8	70.8	73.2	73.6
Females (at birth)	49.0	61.6	73.6	76.8	78.7	79.0

Table 6.7
Source: Adapted from *Social Trends* 25 (1995), Table 7.2 and *Social Trends* 20 (1990), Table 7.2.

Morbidity Rates

Whilst women live longer, they also suffer from more ill health than men. Table 6.9 indicates that women report more illness than men under all the categories for chronic and acute sickness. As is the case with men, however, certain groups of women suffer more illness than others. Figures in the General Household Survey, for instance, suggest that women in the lowest social class group report more than twice the rate of illness than women in the highest group.

Employment status seems to be another factor affecting women's health. With regard to women with children, middle-class women who have paid employment suffer less illness than women from the same class who stay at home, while working-class women with a paid job have worse health than those who do not. Finally, women appear to suffer disproportionately from mental illness, although fewer single women have psychiatric problems than married women (for males the reverse is true—mental health tends to be best among married men).

Towards an Explanation?

Why do women suffer from more health problems than men? Although surveys have suggested that women are more likely to admit to and report illness, three other factors have been highlighted as more significant explanations.

1 *Biological*: Women's role in human reproduction can cause ill health. Pregnancy, childbirth,

Gender Inequalities: Mortality Rates

Death rates per 1,000 population (UK)

	All ages	0–4	5–9	10–14	15–19	20–24	25–34	35–44	45–54	55–64	65–74	75–84	85+
Males	11.5	2.5	0.2	0.3	0.7	0.9	0.9	1.7	5.1	16.0	41.2	96.6	193.9
Females	11.3	1.9	0.2	0.2	0.3	0.3	0.5	1.2	3.2	9.2	23.2	60.4	162.3

Table 6.8
Source: (Adapted from) *Annual Abstract of Statistics 1990* (Table 2.22).

menstruation, contraception, abortion and the menopause all play a part in the greater morbidity rate experienced by women. This is perhaps borne out by the fact that in the younger age groups more males than females report long-standing illness and this trend is only reversed in the 15+ age groups. Moreover, as mentioned above, certain cancers specific to the female gender continue to present significant health risks for women. The increase in the rates of lung cancer among women, at a time when they are beginning to show a decline among men (see figure 6.4), suggests that sex differences in morbidity may widen while differences in mortality may narrow.

2 *Material*: The link between poverty and ill health is well documented, and there is evidence to suggest that women are more likely to suffer from the effects of poverty than men. The reasons for this can be found in women's position in our society. For example, women may have to accept low-paid jobs, head one-parent families, and may be expected to take on the caring role for elderly and disabled relatives. In addition to lack of sufficient money, many women are forced to spend a great deal more of their time at home than men. This makes them more susceptible not only to health problems due to the effects of poor housing conditions, such as dampness, but also to feelings of social isolation which perhaps goes some way to explaining why women suffer from higher rates of mental illness.

3 *Ageing*: 70% of those aged over 75 in the UK

What the **Black Report** Found

1 The *Black Report* found that there are class inequalities in both mortality and morbidity rates and that these inequalities start in childhood and continue throughout life.

2 Subsequent research studies have not only confirmed the findings of the *Black Report* but have suggested that health inequalities have widened since then.

3 The government has argued that social inequalities in health can be explained by the way individuals choose to lead their lives. As a result, it has attempted to change *individual* behaviour and lifestyle through a programme of health education and illness prevention.

4 The *Black Report* and the studies which followed it believe that economic and environmental factors are mainly responsible for social class health inequalities. As a result, they have argued that *collective* action to reduce social and financial inequalities is required.

Chronic and Acute Sickness, 1992

Males Who Reported:	
long-standing illness	31%
limiting long-standing illness	18%
restricted activity	11%
Females Who Reported:	
long-standing illness	33%
limiting long-standing illness	20%
restricted activity	14%

Note: The GHS defines chronic sickness to be a long-standing illness, disability or infirmity, and acute sickness as a restriction of normal activities, as a result of illness or injury, during the two weeks before interview. Informants with a long-standing illness are also asked whether it limits their activities in any way.

Table 6.9
Source: Adapted from *General Household Survey 1992* (Published 1994. Table 3.1).

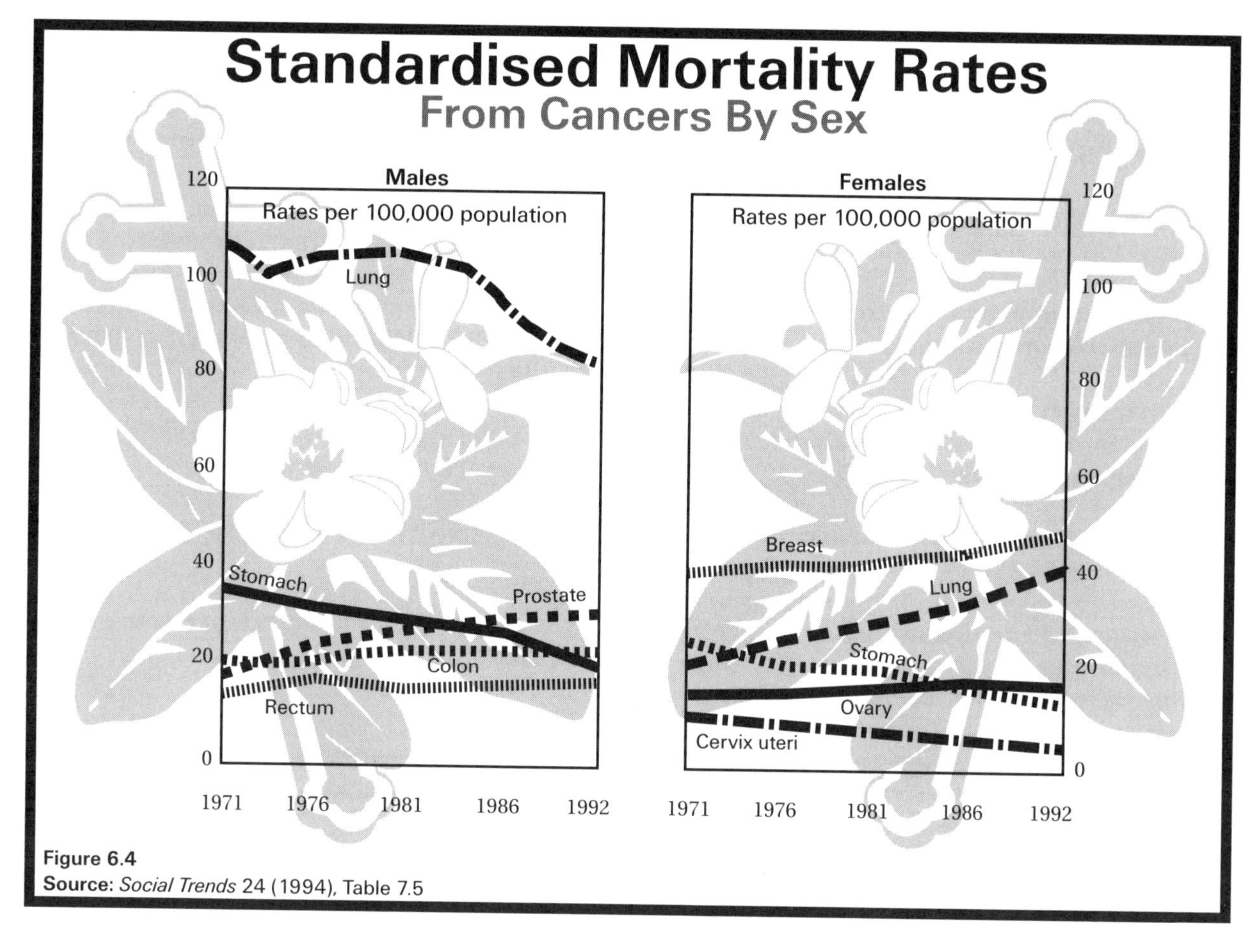

Figure 6.4
Source: *Social Trends* 24 (1994), Table 7.5

are women. Since the elderly experience more ill health than those in younger age groups, it is hardly surprising that proportionately women should have higher rates of morbidity than men. This issue will be explored in much more detail in chapter 7.

ETHNIC INEQUALITIES

Another area in which society is divided in terms of health inequalities is by ethnic origin. Many ethnic minority groups in the UK, especially those who are instantly recognisable as being 'different' due to the colour of their skin, suffer from prejudice and discrimination. If certain groups of people are denied equality of opportunity in areas such as jobs and housing, it is to be expected that this would result in a higher incidence of poverty and that they would experience more ill health than the rest of the population.

As the *Black Report* pointed out, however, official sources such as the census have tended to avoid gathering information on such a sensitive issue as race or ethnic origin. Thus, the research which has been carried out in this area has had to rely on records such as birth and death certificates. This has meant that, with the exception of infant mortality data, the evidence is heavily weighted towards those who were born outside the UK rather than to their descendents. One such piece of re-

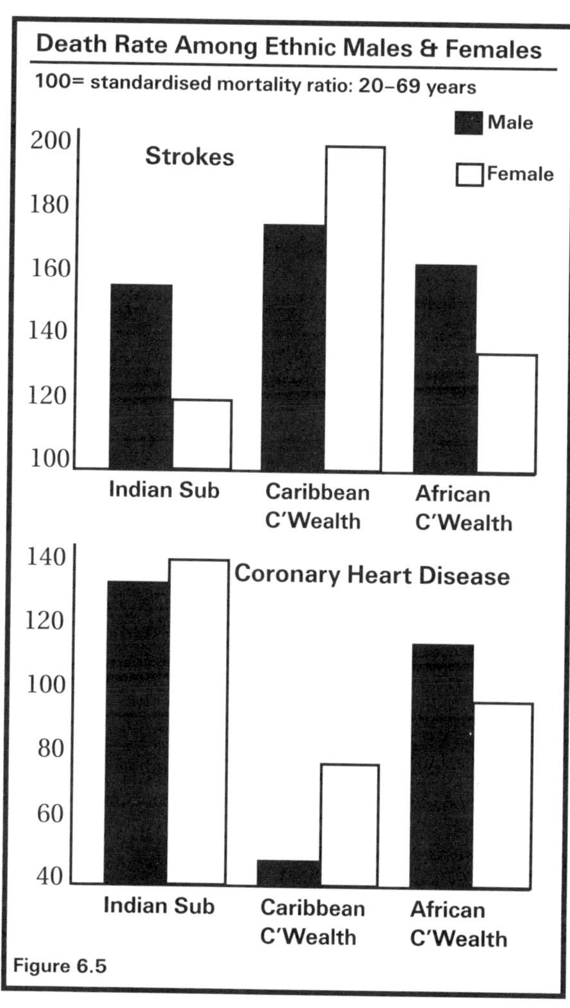

Figure 6.5

The Male-Female Health Divide

Some of the ways Women lose out

1. Women report more illness than men.

2. Women suffer more from respiratory diseases, osteoporosis and cystitis.

3. In the past 40 years, the female death rate from breast cancer has risen in every age group except those under 45.

4. Cases of lung cancer in women have risen by more than 40%.

5. Although heart disease kills more men than women, heart attacks are often more dangerous in women because they have smaller vital arteries to the heart.

Some of the ways Men lose out

1. Men are more likely to smoke, drink too much, take too little exercise and eat a poor diet.

2. Men are half as likely as women to visit a GP.

3. Men are twice as likely as women to die before reaching the age of 65.

4. Three-quarters of all suicides are men.

5. Life expectancy for men is nearly five and a half years less than for women.

search was the *Immigrant Mortality Study in England and Wales* which was published in 1984. The main findings of the study are summarised in the box on page 65.

Immigrant groups tend to have quite different death rate patterns from the rest of the population. You will notice from figure 6.5, that there are significant differences between the various ethnic groups. Indeed, further studies have indicated that mortality rates vary considerably even between different groups from the same sub-continent. For example, Punjabi groups suffer less mortality from cancer than Hindus, with Moslems having the highest rates.

The most detailed research in this area has concentrated on infant mortality rates. The data in figure 6.6 suggests that infant mortality rates are particularly high for babies of mothers born in Pakistan and the Caribbean. Apart from factors such as social class, explanations for these differences have included a higher incidence of anaemia, late childbearing, low maternal height and poor ante-natal attendance. So far, though, there has been little in the way of detailed research into the reasons for the health differences which persist among the ethnic minority groups.

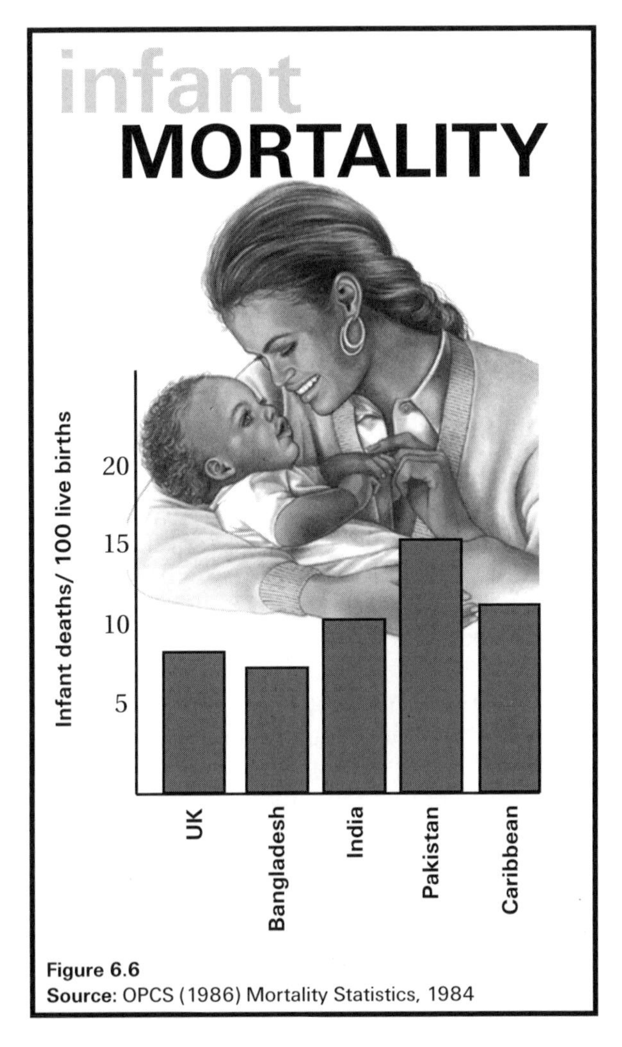

Figure 6.6
Source: OPCS (1986) Mortality Statistics, 1984

Conclusion

Any study which attempts to measure and compare the health of different groups within society is fraught with difficulties. One basic problem confronting researchers is that there is very little routine statistical material on the positive aspects of health. There is, on the other hand, a wealth of data on ill health, death and the use of health services. Relying on such negative indicators of health, however, does not present us with a complete picture. An individual, for instance, might be afflicted by many chronic minor conditions and yet, due to the way that the statistics are gathered, he or she would not be recorded as suffering from ill health. While accepting the general limitations of these statistics, the consensus seems to be that inequalities in health do exist and, in some cases, are widening. In this chapter, geographical, social, gender and ethnic factors were considered separately.

Two points of caution should, however, be made. The first is that not all individuals living in a deprived area or belonging to a disadvantaged group experience more ill health than the population as a whole. The second is that there is an unquestionable overlap between the various factors and that it would, therefore, be a mistake to view them in isolation.

The research would seem to indicate that of all the factors affecting ill health social class and level of income appear to be the most fundamental. If this is in fact so, effective policies which concentrate on wider social conditions, rather than on changing individual behaviour, would seem to be the most constructive approach in attempting to improve the general health of the population.

The Health of Ethnic Groups

good news

- Cancer mortality is lower among all the ethnic groups compared with the general population.
- Most ethnic groups experience lower mortality rates from chronic bronchitis than those born in the UK.
- People from the Caribbean have much lower rates of heart disease than the general population.

bad news

- Infant mortality is higher among the Asian, African and Caribbean communities.
- There is a 36% extra risk of heart disease for men born on the Indian sub-continent, and a 46% extra risk for women, compared with rates for England and Wales as a whole.
- Caribbean men face a 76% greater risk of suffering a stroke than the general population, and women more than double, at 110%.
- Asians have 5 times the rates of diabetes as the general population and people from the Caribbean twice that level.
- Rates of tuberculosis in Indian, Pakistani and Bangladeshi people in the UK are 25 times the rate of infection in the general population.
- The genetic disorder sickle cell anaemia particularly affects people from the Caribbean.

Chapter SEVEN

The Elderly—A Case Study

THE TERMS 'older people' and 'the elderly' are ones with which we are all familiar. Despite their common usage, however, such terms are not particularly helpful in determining exactly what is meant by 'old age'.

The age at which old age is thought to start varies between different cultures and between different historical periods. An individual living in Britain in Victorian times, for instance, would have been considered old at about 40 years of age. Although our perceptions have clearly changed since then, obtaining agreement over how we should define old age has been a much more difficult issue to resolve.

Reflecting Our Age, a study published by Age Concern in 1993, contained the results of a survey on attitudes to old age. It showed that people's ideas of what made someone old depended on their own age. Many 11–14 year-olds believed that old age began in the late 50s; 35–44 year-olds thought it began in the late 60s; those in their mid-60s said it did not begin until the mid-70s.

One of the most common definitions of the elderly is those over statutory retirement age. (At the time of writing, legislation to bring women into line with men by raising their state retirement age from 60 to 65 was going through Parliament.) More recently, there has been a trend towards making a distinction between the 'young' elderly (those aged between 65 and 74 years) and the 'old' elderly (those aged 75 and over).

POPULATION of the UK

(thousands)

1951	1971	1991	2011	2031
50,290	55,298	57,801	61,110	62,096

Table 7.1
Source: Adapted from *Social Trends* 24 (1994), Tables 1.2 and 1.3

If we ignore aspects about the merits of these respective ways of defining the elderly, what is important to note here is that there is no generally accepted definition of when old age begins. The difficulties this causes for researchers when attempting to compare data and interpret trends should always be borne in mind.

AN AGEING POPULATION

Demographic Changes

The population as a whole has grown steadily in recent years (see table 7.1), although this has been at a slower rate than the growth in the number of elderly people. The increase in the proportion of the British population defined as elderly (ie. those of pensionable age) started in the early part of the century and, as you can see from figure 7.1, it has continued to grow steadily in the period since the creation of the NHS.

It is also important, however, to consider the age structure of the elderly population. By the mid-1980s the number of people aged betwen 65–74 had levelled off, but the number of people aged over 75 is expected to increase until the end of the century (see figure 7.2).

Reasons for Change

The increase in both the proportion and the number of elderly people in the population has been the result of two major trends:

1 There has been a dramatic decrease in death rates since the beginning of the century and this has brought about a rise in life expectancy. A man born in 1901 could expect to live on

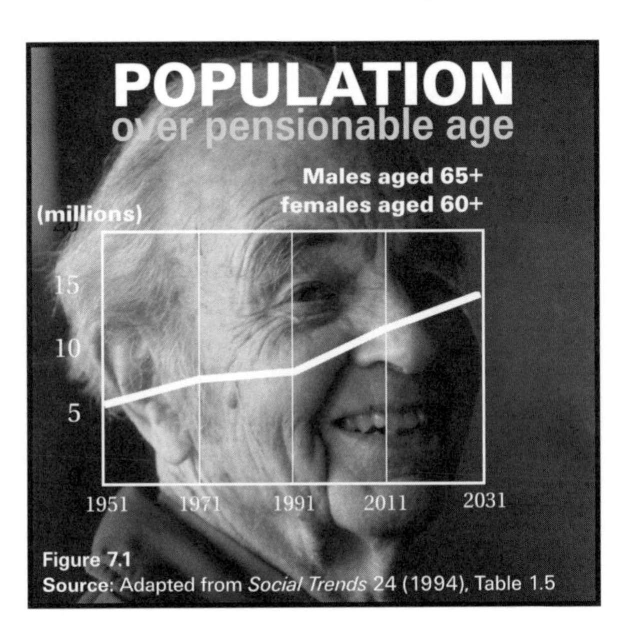

Figure 7.1
Source: Adapted from *Social Trends* 24 (1994), Table 1.5

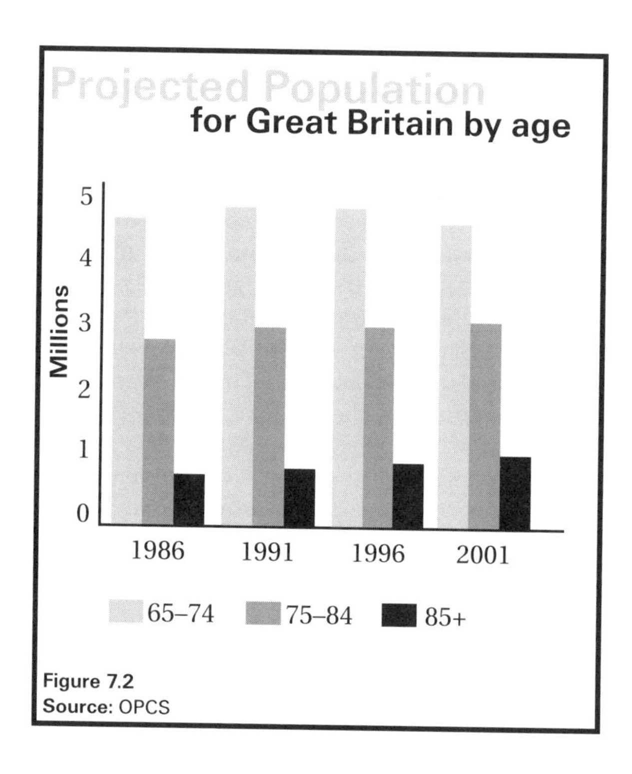

Figure 7.2
Source: OPCS

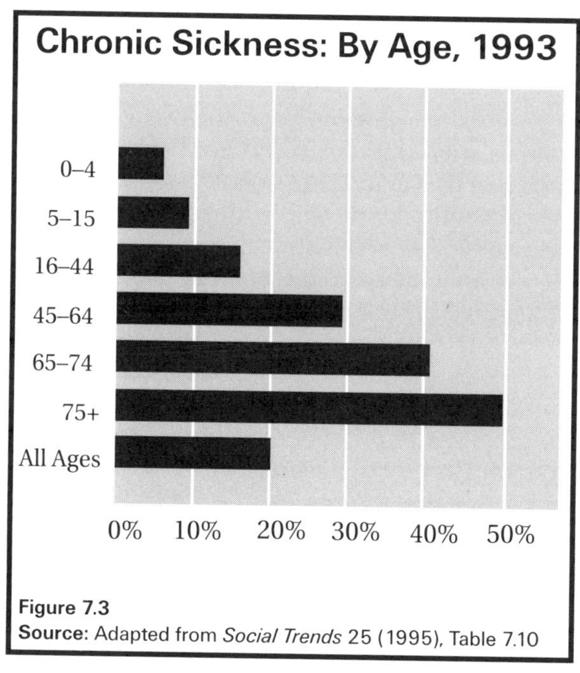

Figure 7.3
Source: Adapted from *Social Trends* 25 (1995), Table 7.10

average only to 46 years and a woman to 49. In 1992, the average lifespan for a man was nearly 74 years and for a woman nearly 79.

2 Although there are annual variations in the fertility or birth rate, the general trend has been for this to decline throughout the century. If fewer people are being born, then it follows that numbers in the younger age groups will be reduced and the *percentage* in the older age groups will be increased.

Implications of Changes

It is the growth in the number of the 'old' elderly which has attracted most interest from politicians and those responsible for health and social policy making. After all, older people do make higher demands on health and personal social services, with those over the age of 75 making the greatest demands of all. For example, in 1991 the NHS spent on average just over £500 per person in the population. However, while it spent only around £250 per person aged between 5 and 64 years, it spent around £900 on every person aged between 65 and 74 and £2,200 on every person aged 75 or over.

Moreover, this is happening at a time when the number of young people in our society is falling which means that there are proportionately fewer people paying taxes to finance these services and, of course, pensions. For example, in 1961 there were almost six people of working age for every person aged over 65. By the year 2011 it is estimated that this ratio will be less than four to one. Not surprisingly then, this demographic shift has brought prophecies of future economic gloom with cuts in both welfare state provision and in living standards generally.

Some researchers, however, have challenged this

Growing Elderly?

The number of people of pensionable age is increasing:

1 In 1991 one person in five in the UK was a pensioner, but it has been estimated that by the year 2020, one-third of the population will be of pensionable age.

2 17.8% of Scotland's population was of pensionable age in 1993 (which was more than the 15% of schoolchildren).

Within this group, the numbers of 'old' elderly are increasing at a faster rate:

1 Between 1992 and 2001 the total number of people aged 65 and over in the country is expected to increase by less than 3%. The number aged 75 and over is expected to increase by 10.5%.

2 In 1951 there were 300 people who received a Telemessage from the Queen due to reaching 100 years of age, while in 1991 there were 4,390 (all but 500 of whom were women).

Acute Sickness

Average number of days sick per person per year, by age, UK, 1992

Age	Number of Days
0-4	13
5-15	11
16-44	18
45-64	31
65-74	44
75+	59

Table 7.2
Source: *General Household Survey* 1992 (OPCS 1994)

view. They have argued that if the long-term trend of declining birth rates continues, less money may need to be spent on child health care and on education in the future and, as a result, these resources could be diverted towards the provision of care for the elderly. It has also been suggested that with properly targeted health promotion and illness prevention policies and the development of services which emphasise provision of temporary—rather than long-term—support at times of illness, the elderly can be encouraged to stay reasonably healthy and to remain independent for longer. Such initiatives would also help to greatly reduce the costs of their care.

Before going on to examine the type and nature of provision on offer, let us first of all briefly consider the health status of the elderly.

THE HEALTH OF THE ELDERLY

Difficulties Involved in such a Study

1 There is a danger in making generalisations about the health of the elderly. The term 'ageism' has recently become an accepted addition to the English language. Like 'racism' or 'sexism' it is used to describe discriminatory images against all members of a particular group. Those who are guilty of 'ageism' then, see the elderly as being all alike, often in a negative sense. They may believe, for example, that all elderly people suffer from the same problems such as deteriorating mental abilities and poor health. Such stereotyped or distorted images should always be resisted since, as we shall see, they often bear little resemblance to reality.

2 As was discussed in Chapter 6, health is a difficult concept to define. Statistical material tends to record health in a negative way, for instance highlighting mortality and ill health, rather than measuring it in a more positive sense. To assume that individuals not recorded as suffering from ill health must therefore be healthy is highly questionable. Although the data in this section relies heavily on these negative measures of health, it is once again important to stress that their limitations should be kept firmly in mind.

The Evidence

When studying morbidity (or ill health), researchers have increasingly differentiated between short-term (or acute) health problems and those of a more long-standing (or chronic) nature. Not surprisingly, the evidence would suggest that older people report both more acute and more chronic sickness than do younger adults.

1 Acute health problems include conditions such as colds, influenza and accidental injuries. Each year the General Household Survey asks people questions about acute sickness. Using this data, table 7.2 reveals that as people grow older, there is an increase in the number of days during which they suffer from acute illness.

2 Chronic health problems include long-standing illnesses or disabilities such as arthritis, rheumatism and heart conditions. Using data from the General Household Survey (see table 7.3), we can see that the percentage reporting chronic sickness increases with age.

Moreover when the elderly population is broken down further into even more specific age bands (see table 7.3), it seems that chronic ill health becomes more common as age increases. What these figures also indicate, however, is that not all old people suffer from chronic ill health. Indeed, even in the 85 years or over age group, the category who are most prone to health problems, almost one-

Chronic Sickness

reported long-standing illness by age, 1985 (%)

Persons aged 65+

	65–69	70–74	75–79	80–84	85+	All 65+
Total with long-standing illness	54	56	61	62	68	58
No long-standing illness	46	44	39	38	32	42

Table 7.3
Source: Adapted from *General Household Survey*, 1986 (OPCS 1988) Table 12.7

Health in General By Sex & Age, UK 1985

	65–74	75+	Total
Good			
Men	46	38	44
Women	41	34	38
All Elderly	43	35	40
Fairly Good			
Men	33	40	35
Women	37	38	37
All Elderly	35	39	37
Not Good			
Men	20	22	21
Women	22	28	25
All Elderly	21	26	23

Table 7.4
Source: Adapted from *General Household Survey* 1986, (OPCS 1988) Table 12.6

Healthy Elderly?

1 39% of people aged 65–75 suffer a long-standing illness or disability which limits their activity. This increases to 51% of people aged 75 and over (*General Household Survey* 1992).

2 43% of those aged 75 and over have difficulty hearing (*General Household Survey* 1992).

3 90% of people with visual impairment are aged 60 and over (*Blind and Partially Sighted Adults in Britain Survey* 1991).

4 Almost one-quarter of people aged over 100 have no limiting long-term illness (1991 Census).

third of those surveyed reported no long-standing disability or illness.

As you can see from table 7.4, when individuals were asked to evaluate their own health nearly 80% of those aged over 65 regarded themselves as having 'good' or 'fairly good' health. As one would perhaps expect, given the higher incidence of chronic sickness, the 'old' elderly category were more likely to rate their health as 'not good' than the 'young' elderly. What is surprising though, is that so few of the elderly regarded their health as 'not good' when the data in table 7.2 and figure 7.3 suggests that they do, in fact, suffer from much higher rates of illness.

One explanation which has been provided for this anomaly is that people tend to compare their health status with their own peers rather than with people in other age groups. In other words, an individual's expectation of what makes good health becomes less demanding the older he or she gets. Another possible explanation is that the elderly, whether they are aware of it or not, tend to refuse to accept the label of being sick as a way of denying the traditional stereotype of ill health being an inevitable feature of old age.

Like the population as a whole, the elderly are a varied collection of people. Some of the data in the preceding tables illustrates some of the health differences experienced by elderly people and, of course, there are also considerable variations between men and women, between different areas of the country and between different ethnic groups. Furthermore, the *Black Report* suggested that inequalities in health among the elderly are also the result of differences in social class. Not only do manual workers' bodies wear out sooner than those of non-manual workers, but material well-being, or the lack of it, in old age is closely linked with occupational class during working life. Table 7.5 illustrates this association between occupational class and the health of the elderly.

Conclusion

Although the old do tend to suffer from more ill health than the young, it is clear from the evidence that the zimmer frame and wheelchair image of the elderly is far from the truth. In part, the pro-

Chronic Sickness

reported long-standing illness by sex, age, and socio-economic group (UK 1992)

Socio-economic group of head of household	Males 65+	Females 65+
Professional	49%	61%
Employers & Managers	57%	60%
Intermediate non-manual	63%	61%
Junior non-manual	59%	63%
Skilled manual	64%	63%
Semi-skilled manual	63%	64%
Unskilled manual	66%	64%

Table 7.5
Source: Adapted from *General Household Survey* 1992, (OPCS 1994) Table 3.2

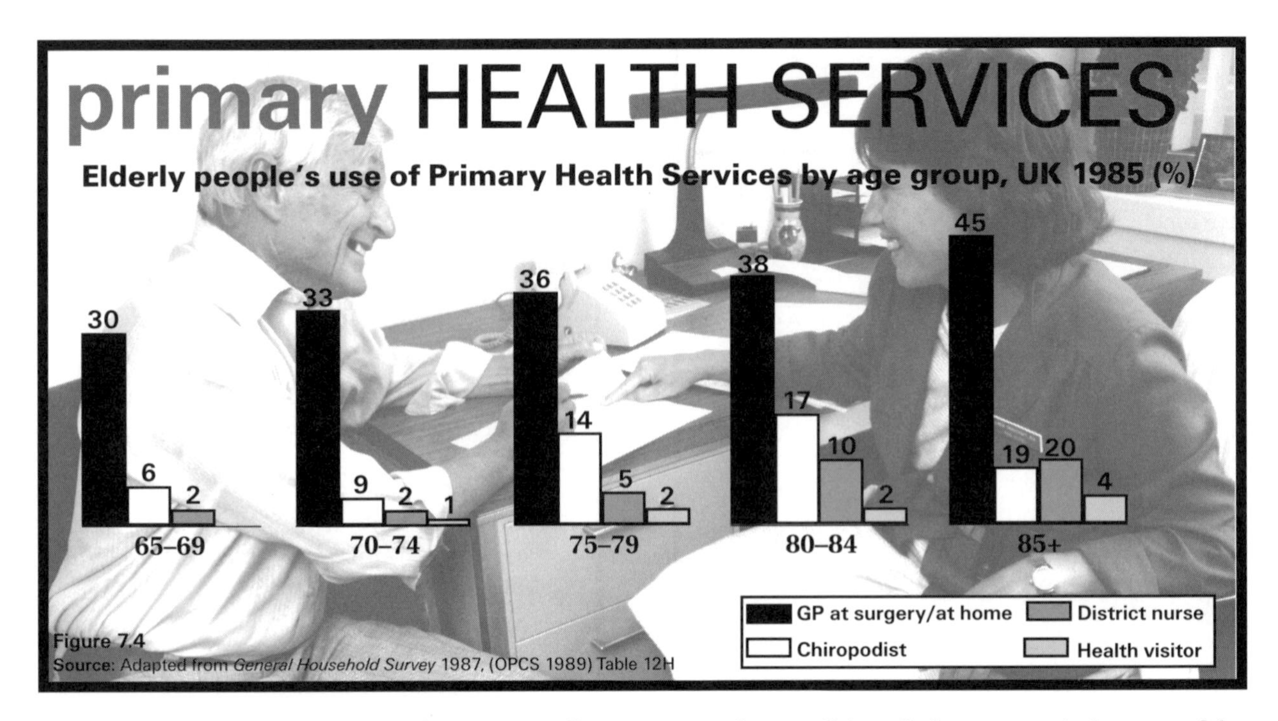

Figure 7.4
Source: Adapted from *General Household Survey* 1987, (OPCS 1989) Table 12H

fessionals—the medical and social services staff—have contributed to the continuance of this myth. Perhaps it is understandable that many of them should believe that old equals ill when the only elderly people they are in contact with are those who do have health problems. The reality, though, is that the health and social services touch on only a minority of old people. As was mentioned earlier, the development of services which best meet the needs of the elderly, both individually and collectively, can only occur when such old-fashioned ideas of old age are done away with.

HEALTH SERVICES FOR THE ELDERLY

As we have seen, the National Health Service Acts of 1946 and 1947 set up a comprehensive health service for everyone regardless of their means. There is little argument that the wide range of largely free health care services provided for the elderly have gone a long way to remove many of the fears previously associated with ill health.

The provision of health care for the elderly, however, has traditionally been regarded as one of the so-called 'Cinderella' services. A number of government-sponsored Reports and White Papers have been published with the aim of developing policies which would improve the standard of care offered to the elderly. To see whether these policies have had any impact, or whether indeed,older people continue to receive inequality of treatment compared to other age groups, a brief examination of the various health services provided for the elderly will be necessary.

GP Consultations

Average number of GP consultations per person per year

All Persons	1992
16–44	4
45–64	5
65–74	6
75+	7

Table 7.6
Source: Adapted from *General Household Survey* 1992, (OPCS 1994) Table 3.10

Primary Health Care

The General Practitioner is at the centre of primary health services and since 1948 every person in the community has had the right to be registered with a NHS GP practice. Also included in this category are chiropodists, district nurses and health visitors.

Older people have more consultations with GPs than do younger adults (see table 7.6). As might be expected, moreover, elderly people are more likely to require to be visited at home by their GP than are the young. Although the other primary health care services were not developed specifically with the elderly in mind, older people do make considerable use of them. Evidence from the General Household Survey (see figure 7.4) shows that the proportions of elderly people using the various primary health services increases the older they get.

There were a number of developments in the late 1980s, particularly in the delivery of GP services, which had a direct effect on elderly patients.

1 There has been a distinct movement away from single-doctor practices towards doctors

Group practice in modern Health Centres benefits some patients but not all.

grouping themselves together in health centres. This has turned out to be something of a mixed blessing for many older people. On the one hand, these purpose-built group practices and health centres can offer their patients the whole range of primary health care services under the one roof. On the other hand, many elderly people have found that access to their GP has become more difficult. For one thing, many patients have to travel longer distances to visit their GP. This particularly affects the elderly as not only do old people tend to have greater mobility problems, but they also rely more on public transport than the rest of the population. Furthermore, group practices are usually organised on a rigid appointment system and this can create difficulties for older people who are statistically less likely to have a telephone than the population as a whole.

2 As we saw in Chapter 4, the new GP Contract stipulated that GPs were to be responsible for ensuring that each of their patients over the age of 75 was screened annually. Whilst some have argued that this requirement is not the best way of using the time of busy GPs, others have argued that this is likely to be of significant benefit to some elderly people as it will inevitably lead to earlier intervention and diagnosis of illnesses.

3 As we also saw, 'indicative' drug budgets were allocated to all GP practices, while large practices were allowed to take control of their own budgets to buy selected services for their patients. The government and its supporters have claimed that these changes have helped to contain costs while, at the same time, creating greater consumer choice and an overall improvement in the standard of health care. For example, GP fundholders have been able to use savings from their budgets to provide new services, such as physiotherapy and dietary advice, which have been of great benefit to their elderly patients. Critics, on the other hand, have argued that the reforms have changed the priorities of GPs and that now their major consideration is to keep within their budgets. This change in emphasis has meant that they have

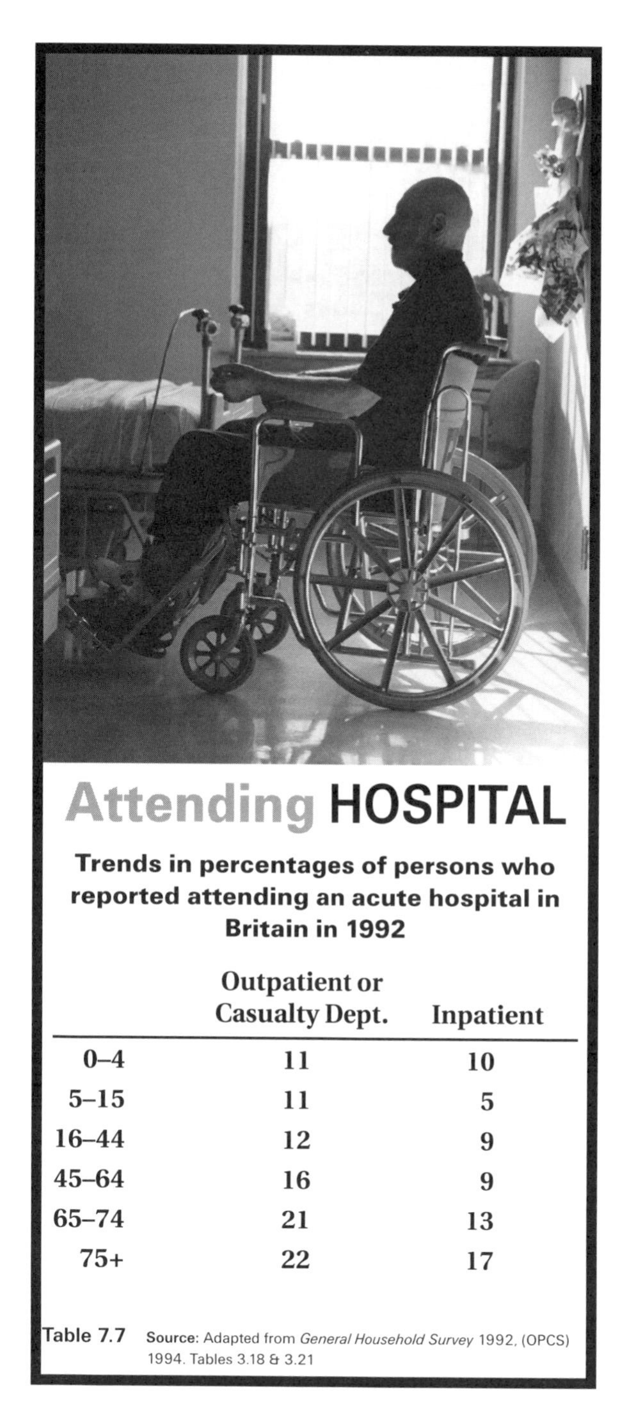

Attending HOSPITAL

Trends in percentages of persons who reported attending an acute hospital in Britain in 1992

	Outpatient or Casualty Dept.	Inpatient
0–4	11	10
5–15	11	5
16–44	12	9
45–64	16	9
65–74	21	13
75+	22	17

Table 7.7 Source: Adapted from *General Household Survey* 1992, (OPCS) 1994. Tables 3.18 & 3.21

been discouraged from taking on potentially expensive patients such as the elderly.

Moreover, since only fundholding GPs can use savings to improve the services in their practices, elderly patients of non-fundholders are disadvantaged in comparison to patients of fundholders.

Hospital Services

One of the most commonly held myths about the elderly is that the ageing process inevitably create health problems and that, as a result, a large number of old people end up in hospital. The reality, however, is that, on average, under 3% of elderly people are in hospital at any one time. What cannot be denied, however, is that elderly people

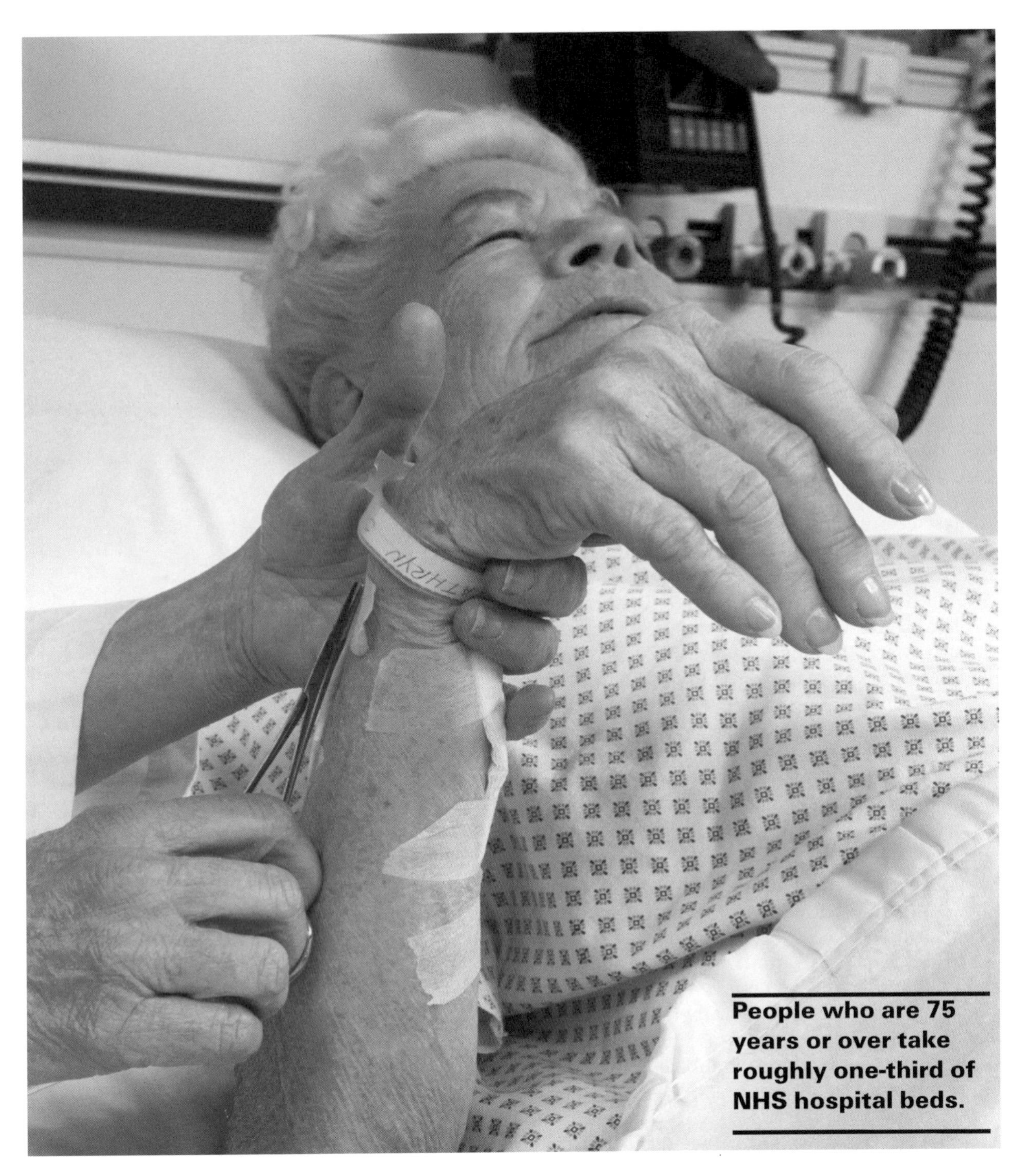

People who are 75 years or over take roughly one-third of NHS hospital beds.

do, proportionately, make more use of hospital beds and stay in hospital longer than younger people. In fact, people who are aged 75 years or over take up roughly one-third of all NHS hospital beds.

Elderly patients are accommodated in an extremely confusing variety of hospital settings. They occupy beds in geriatric or speciality wards (such as general surgery or orthopaedic) in acute hospitals, on a short-term basis in day hospitals, and in the institutional sector, such as in long-stay geriatric hospitals, residential and nursing homes. To further complicate matters, some hospitals are provided through the NHS, some by local authorities, some by voluntary and charitable bodies and some by the private sector.

Acute Hospital Services

The elderly are more prone to sudden and acute illness than younger adults, so it is hardly surprising that they are the main client group for acute hospital care (see table 7.7). Indeed, more than half of the total hospital workload in the acute sector involves people aged 65 or over. One of the most commonly held stereotyped views of hospital care for the old is that the majority of elderly hospital patients are in geriatric long-stay hospitals. In any given year, however, there are more old people who are patients in acute hospitals than there are geriatric patients. Consequently then, any attempt to look at the resources available for the hospital care of the elderly has to consider the acute sector closely.

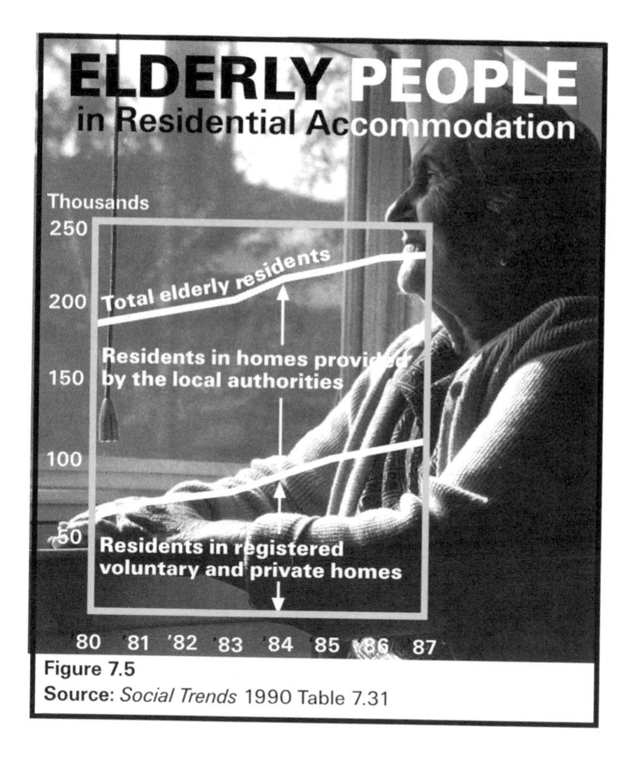

Figure 7.5
Source: *Social Trends* 1990 Table 7.31

It is often claimed that the increasing number and proportion of elderly people in the population is likely to place the acute hospital sector under a severe strain in coming years. The impact will be felt in several ways:

1 Older patients tend to stay longer in acute hospitals than younger patients. Often this is because they cannot be discharged from hospital since there is no other suitable accommodation available for them. This so-called 'bed-blocking' means that there are fewer acute hospital beds available for emergencies. The length of stay in hospitals has decreased markedly in recent years, but the continuing ageing of the population has meant that NHS policy makers have had to find further ways of making reductions.

2 Recent government reports have shown that in some acute hospitals there are not enough night nurses to perform essential tasks. Demographic changes are likely to make such shortages even worse. The number of cases treated involving elderly people is rising at the same time as the number of girls leaving school—a traditional recruiting ground for nurses—is going down.

3 The estimated increase in the number of elderly patients will mean serious financial implications for the NHS. The average cost of health care for individuals aged between 65 and 74 is two and a half times as much as it is for those individuals aged between 15 and 64. For individuals over the age of 75, the cost of providing health care rises to seven times the cost of caring for and looking after patients who are under 64.

What effects has the introduction of the internal market had on elderly hospital patients? Once again, two conflicting views can be determined:

1 The government and its supporters have argued that the internal market has improved the overall standard of health care for the elderly. For example, providers of health care services have been encouraged to move resources into services which purchasers have demanded. As a result, many elderly patients have been able to benefit from improvements in services such as chiropody and physiotherapy. Also, since purchasers can shop around for services, many elderly patients can avoid long waiting lists in their local hospital by travelling to another hospital in another area.

Moreover, Trust hospitals have proved to be more efficient than non-Trusts and this has meant that many elderly patients have had to wait shorter times for operations such as hip replacements and the removal of cataracts.

2 Critics of the reforms, however, have claimed that the changes have resulted in a much inferior service for many elderly patients. For one thing, the separation of responsibilities for purchasing and providing health services may restrict the freedom of some elderly patients to be treated in the hospital of their choice since purchasers can only buy services from those hospitals with which they have a contract. Also, the pressure on Trust hospitals to increase their number of patient treatments has resulted in patients spending less time in hospital. The problem with this is that if people are sent home quicker, they may also be sent home sicker. For the 'old' elderly, who are more likely to stay alone, such a practice may well lead to rapid readmission to hospital or even perhaps to permanent institutionalisation.

Residential accommodation

There are three main providers of residential homes for the elderly:

Local authorities. Part III of the Public Assistance Act (1946) gave powers to the local authorities to provide residential homes for old people. These have become known as 'Part III' accommodation.

Voluntary or charitable bodies. These homes very often cater for particular groups of the elderly such as the widows of the clergy.

Private sector. These are run along commercial lines and include privately-run hospitals and nursing homes as well as more basic residential establishments.

As you can see from figure 7.5, a third of elderly people in residential accommodation were in registered voluntary and private homes in 1980, while by 1987 this had risen to about a half. Most of this increase had been due to a large-scale growth in the private sector. There have been several factors which have brought about this unprecedented expansion in the provision of private rest and nursing homes:

1 The most important single reason was the change in the ideological climate during the 1980s. As we have seen, the Conservative administrations elected since 1979 were committed to the principles of individual responsibility, the encouragement of the free market and the expansion of the private sector.

2 The Conservative administration's commitment to reduce public expenditure and to control the spending of local authorities brought about a virtual standstill in the construction of local authority residential homes during the 1980s. This was happening, of course, at a time when the numbers of old people were increasing. Recognising the extent of this unmet and growing need, the private sector enthusiastically expanded its share of the market.

3 The government openly encouraged privately run residential care by meeting the cost of board and lodging for elderly social security claimants. In fact, DSS payments to old people in residential and nursing homes rose from £7 million in 1978 (the year before the Conservatives came into power) to a massive £2,000 million in 1992.

4 The richest pickings for the private sector, however, are in the provision of luxury residential care. Here the industry has been greatly assisted by a general rise in old people's living standards. In the 1950s the disposable income of the average pensioner was 40% of that of a non-pensioner, while by the late 1980s this had risen to 70%. The great attraction of the private luxury home sector is their hotel-type facilities. Some of these upmarket homes also provide good medical facilities on site, while others only provide nursing care. Typically, private nursing homes are run by a husband-and-wife team based in their converted home or previously unprofitable guest house.

It is hardly surprising, then, that there is a wide variation in quality within the private residential sector. Some homes provide an excellent standard of care; others are overcrowded, understaffed and run by people without appropriate training or qualifications. What was of more concern to the government, however, was the enormous rise in the public subsidy to the residential care sector. It was this which prompted it to look at alternative ways of caring for the elderly.

CARE IN THE COMMUNITY

The government's proposed solution to the problem was to introduce reforms to the way in which community care was financed and delivered. Before looking at these changes, however, it is worth considering the debate which has arisen over the meaning of the term 'community care', the reasons why successive governments have supported policies based on care in the community and the way in which these policies have developed over the years.

What is Community Care?

The term 'community care' has been in common usage for at least as long as the NHS itself. Despite this passage of time, there remains a great deal of confusion about what the term actually means.

The problem does not lie with the fundamental objective of community care. Here there is general agreement that government policy in this area should be directed at attempting to switch the balance of care for the elderly (and other so-called dependent groups such as the mentally ill and those with learning difficulties or physical disabilities) from institutions to a more flexible range of community-based services. Rather, the confusion over the meaning of community care has centred on who is to provide this care and how it is to be organised.

1 Some view community care as care ***in*** the community. Those who agree with this definition believe that the emphasis of policy should be di-

Caring FOR People

Main Objectives

1. To clarify responsibilities for the planning and coordinating of community care.
2. To encourage a 'mixed economy' of welfare.
3. To promote a wider choice of services which would allow people to remain in their own homes whenever possible.
4. To devise high quality care based on individual needs assessment.
5. To create a system which would bring better value for money.
6. To offer support for carers.

Main Proposals

1. Local authority social services departments given the lead responsibility for community care.
2. The separation of purchasing and providing roles.
3. Local authorities expected to use voluntary and private providers as well as their own services.
4. Assessment of individual needs and case managers to arrange individually tailored packages of care.
5. Assessment of clients' ability to help pay for the care they receive.
6. Local authorities given a fixed budget to cover the cost of social care, whether this was in people's own homes or in residential care. In 1992 the government decided to 'ring-fence' the community care budget for four years.

rected towards the provision of an extensive range of both health and social services. In other words, health services such as chiropody, district nurses and health visitors, and social services such as home helps, meals on wheels and day centres, should be the main providers of support and care for the elderly in their homes.

2 Others see community care as care *by* the community. The implication behind this view is that, while the public sector may still have a role, the main support for keeping the elderly out of institutions should be provided by an informal network of family, friends and neighbours. Before 1979, the official view of community care was closer to the first of these definitions. As we shall see, however, after that the emphasis shifted to the latter definition. The main reason was that this definition best fitted the Conservative government's philosophy with its belief in the virtues of self-reliance and its desire to reduce the role of the state in the provision of welfare.

Why Community Care?

The concept of community care has received widespread political, professional and public support. Several factors have contributed to this rather unusual degree of approval.

1. During the 1960s, a number of well-publicised allegations of low standards of treatment, and even the ill-treatment, of elderly patients in several long-stay hospitals helped to discredit the image of the institutional care sector.

2. At a time of significant demographic changes it was becoming more and more difficult to attract sufficient numbers of suitably qualified residential staff.

3 There was a great deal of concern being expressed that many elderly patients admitted to acute hospitals remained there long after their treatment had been completed simply because there was nowhere else for them to go. The development of community care would enable many of these patients to be discharged and would help to prevent 'bed-blocking' of this type.

4 The so-called drug revolution of the 1950s was seen as offering a possible solution to treating people in the community rather than in an institution.

5 The moral claim that people's quality of life would be improved if they were taken out of institutional care and placed back in the community became more widely accepted.

6 The economic argument that, unlike institutional care which was a very expensive method of treating patients, community care would be a much cheaper option. Although there has been a great deal of academic debate over the validity of this claim, the economic argument has been the most powerful force behind the development of community care.

Moving Towards Community Care

The arguments in favour of community care were both moral and financial. Not surprisingly, then, from the mid-1970s onwards, official documents, most with the words 'community' or 'care' in their title, began to highlight support for the concept of keeping dependent groups, including the elderly, out of institutional care.

It was a 1986 report from the Audit Commission, *Making Reality of Community Care*, which finally stung the government into action. The report noted that community based services were not being developed very rapidly and were not being provided by all local authorities. It also highlighted the fact that the social security system gave no incentive for these services to be developed since income support was offered for residential provision but not for community care. According to the Audit Commission, instead of the elderly being cared for in their own homes at low cost, social security payments were spiralling out of control as they were having to finance the much more expensive institutional care for the elderly in private residential homes.
The government turned to Sir Roy Griffiths, Mrs Thatcher's personal adviser on health care who, as we saw in Chapter 3, had previously presided over a report on the management structure of the NHS. His remit was to investigate ways of streamlining the organisation and funding of community care. As we have seen, the main reason for him being asked to produce the report was the government's growing concern over the spiralling cost of social security payments to keep people in residential care.

His report, *Community Care: Agenda for Action*, was published early in 1988. It described community care as the poor relation of the health service, concluding that much of the £6 billion budget allocated for the care of the elderly and other dependent groups was being misspent. The report argued that the incentive to admit people to residential care should be removed and that a wider range of services should be made available to those in need. Its remedy included the following recommendations.

1 Under the system which then was in place, responsibility for funding community care was divided between the NHS, local authorities and social security. According to Griffiths, such a system was "almost designed to produce patchy performance" and meant that community care had become "everybody's distant relative, but nobody's baby". Consequently, he suggested that the local authorities should take over the leading role as co-ordinators and organisers of the service.

2 The report argued that the least complex way of financing community care would be to give local authorities protected or, using the current jargon, 'ring-fenced' funds from central government. This would amount to between 40 and 50% of the cost of the programme, and the local au-

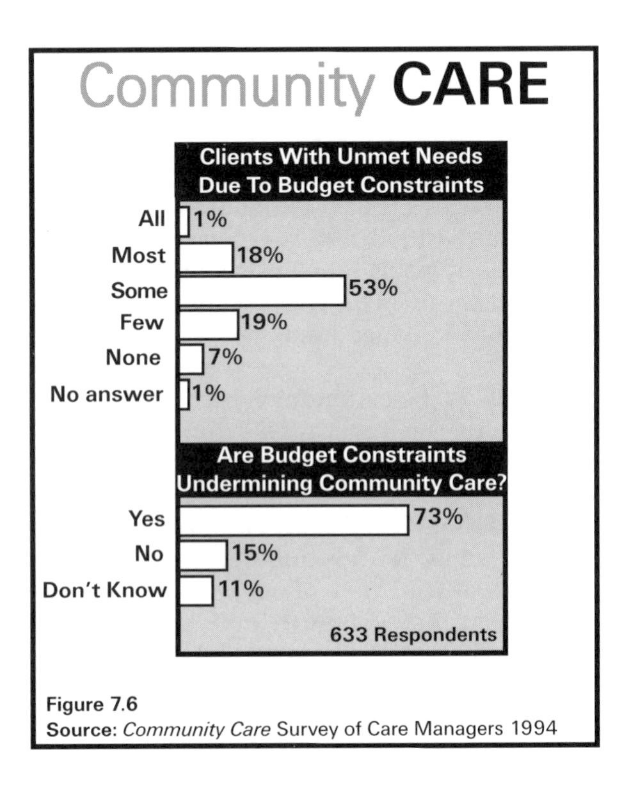

Figure 7.6
Source: *Community Care* Survey of Care Managers 1994

thorities would make up the remainder from the poll tax and charges.

3 Social work services should implement an assessment programme aimed at keeping as many people as possible in the community and out of residential care. Social workers would, for the first time, be given budgets to buy care tailored to each patient's needs, and this would include services from the public, private and voluntary sectors. The report stated, "social service authorities should see themselves as arrangers and purchasers of care services—not as monopolistic providers."

4 A new Minister of State, with overall responsibility for standards and the setting of objectives for the service, should be appointed.

The Government Acts on Community Care

A number of Griffiths' proposals for community care reform caused the government considerable discomfort. In particular, the recommendation to give local authorities the leading role was never likely to go down well with a government which had never sought to hide its dislike of local government whom it had continually criticised as spendthrifts and had traditionally feared as potential centres of opposition.

The government was to wrestle with its anxieties for 16 months before it felt able to respond with the publication of its White Paper *Caring for People* in November 1989.

According to Kenneth Clarke, the then Secretary of State for Health, the White Paper was "eighty per cent Griffiths". Indeed, *Caring for People* did agree with the Griffiths Report on the following important points.

- Local authorities to become the leading agencies in the planning of community care.
- Clients no longer to receive payments for their residential care from the social security budget. Instead, the money would be administered by the local authorities social service departments.
- A 'mixed market' of care to be developed through the separation of the purchaser and provider roles. Some social care services would continue to be provided by local authorities, but increasingly they would be expected to act as enablers, buying services from the voluntary and private sectors rather than being direct providers of services themselves.
- The principle of case management was to be the 'cornerstone' of the new system. Each person requiring care was to be assessed before their individual care package was prepared.

Although the White Paper was based on Griffiths' recommendations, there were key differences between them. The most notable of these were:

- The Griffiths Report proposed that funds transferred to local government should be ring-fenced for their intended purpose of developing community care services, but this was rejected by the government. In the face of strong opposition, however, the government made a U-turn on this issue in 1992 when it announced that—for a period of four years only—local authorities would not be able to use for any other purpose, central government funds earmarked for community care.
- The idea that there should be a minister responsible for all aspects of community care was not accepted by the government.
- The Griffiths Report argued that services from providers in the private sector should be bought in where it was clearly more efficient or cost effective than public provision, but the White Paper went much further when it advocated the replacement of public services by the private sector. During the implementation of the reforms the government added the requirement that local authorities had to allocate 85% of any new money they received from central government towards services provided by the private sector.
- The original remit of Griffiths had only been for England and Wales, but the government decided that the plans should be widened to include Scotland.

The White Paper was followed by legislation in the form of *The National Health Service and Community Care Act* which received Royal Assent in June 1990 (Parts III and IV of the Act referred to community care, while the earlier parts contained the NHS Review policies —see Chapter 4). The community care legislation was to take effect in April 1991.

The issue of financing the programme, however, continued to concern the government. Estimates for the cost of the first 18 months of implementation ran at £500 million. Such an expenditure would, it was claimed, have added an extra £15 per head to the increasingly unpopular poll tax. Following several weeks of speculation, the government finally put the brakes on the programme in July 1990 when it announced its decision to postpone implementation of the bulk of commu-

NUMBER OF PEOPLE in Nursing and Residential Care

	1993	1994
NHS long-stay beds	56,000	51,000
Private nursing homes	159,000	164,000
Private residential homes	152,000	150,000
Voluntary & nursing residential homes	61,000	60,000
Local authority homes	84,000	77,000
Total	512,000	502,000

Table 7.8 **Source:** Adapted from *Care of Elderly People Market Survey*, Laing and Buisson 1995

nity care policies until 1993.

Implementing Community Care: An Assessment

The main thrust of the government's community care reforms—to promote home-based alternatives to institutional and residential care in order to allow maximum independence and more choice—was seen by many as both desirable and overdue. A great deal of concern, however, was expressed over a number of issues involved in the detailed implementation of the changes. At the time of writing, just two years into the reforms, it is only possible to make some initial observations on the changes to see whether or not these fears were justified.

1 *Adequate Funding?* In the first year (1993–94), over £660 million was transferred from the social security budget to local authorities in England, Wales and Scotland to help to implement the community care reforms; in the following year this was increased to over £750 million. At a time of tight public spending limits this was promoted by the government as an extremely generous settlement.

The associations representing local authorities, however, viewed these sums as amounting to a shortfall of some £200 million for each of the two years and raised the concern that, as a result, many individuals, even if they had been assessed as being in need, would not get their needs met. The results of a survey of care managers undertaken by the magazine *Community Care* in 1994 seems to suggest that there was substance to these concerns (see figure 7.6). There is also evidence that some social service departments have experienced severe financial difficulties. For example:

- Surrey ran out of money before the end of the financial year and asked private residential and nursing homes to accommodate people who were the local authority's responsibility at no charge for a few months.
- Gloucestershire was taken to the High Court by 5 disabled pensioners for cutting services it could no longer afford to provide.

The Gloucestershire case was seen as an important one for the future financing of community care. If the High Court had found against Gloucestershire, the implication would have been that local authorities would have had a requirement to meet all unmet need. This in turn would have put pressure on the government to provide more money for community care services. In the event the judgement, announced in June 1995, declared that the council was wrong to cut its community care services indiscriminately but that it could and should take resources into account both in the assessment of need and in the provision of services.

As a result, community care will in future be resources-led rather than needs-led. This is likely to leave many vulnerable people without adequate care and will mean that, in effect, a community care waiting list will be created.

It is extremely unlikely that there will be the same political pressure on the government to reduce this list as there is with the hospital waiting list.

2 *The Effects of Privatisation?* The introduction of the community care system was intended to steer people away from care in residential settings. It was also hoped that the changes would help promote the private sector. As you can see from table 7.8, the evidence from the first year of the new system seems to suggest that both of these objectives are succeeding. While the total number of people in nursing and residential care fell by 10,000 between 1993 and 1994—the first reduction since statistics were first collected more than thirty years ago—this fall was achieved almost entirely at the expense of NHS beds and places in local authority homes.
The other main objective of the reforms was to expand the range and improve the quality of community care services. The government's insistence

that 85 per cent of residential care should be provided by the independent sector has meant that many local authority homes for the elderly have had to be closed. Not only has this reduced the range of alternative services, but in many cases it has meant that well-established statutory quality care has been replaced by an uncoordinated patchwork of independent facilities. On the other hand, one of the most striking changes since the reforms came in has been the rapid development of the independent domiciliary care sector. There is an increasing acceptance that without making greater use of these independent providers, local authorities would be unable to meet the growing demand for home care.

3 *Health or Social Care?* One of the main aims of the reforms was to clear up the confusion over who was responsible for what with regard to community care. It attempted to do this by replacing the system whereby responsibility for funding community care was shared by the NHS, social security and local authorities by allocating most of the responsibility to the local authorities.

Critics have argued, however, that confusion over boundaries remains since there is a failure in the new arrangements to give clear definitions of health care on the one hand and social care on the other. This omission is an important one for two reasons.

a) At a time when health boards and local authorities are confronted with limited resources and unmet need, there is a real possibility that they will attempt to offload their responsibilities onto one another or, worse still, that vulnerable people will fall between the two and receive no care at all.

b) While health care is provided by the NHS free of charge, social care is provided on a means-tested basis for which patients may well have to pay. Indeed, it has been estimated that over 40,000 elderly couples a year are being forced to sell their homes to finance long-term care bills (see newspaper article *The Price of Growing Old*).

In an attempt to clarify the situation, in February 1995 the government published guidance on the care of the elderly and long-term sick. It emphasised the commitment of the NHS to provide long-term care for those who need it, but it introduced a new power which allows hospitals to discharge patients who do not want to move to a nursing or residential home because of the expense. Previously, patients had the right to refuse to leave hospital, but in future they may be forced to move back into their homes with a package of community care services. It is likely that they will have to pay at least part of the cost of these services. The distinction between health care and social care was retained.The decisions about what type of care a patient is entitled to being made according to locally determined criteria, that is health boards and authorities in consultation with local authorities. The guidelines were due to come into effect in April 1996. The recognition in the guidelines that the NHS still had a responsibility for long-term care was widely welcomed. There was con-

THE PRICE OF GROWING OLD

IN HIS first speech as Tory Leader to the Party's conference in 1991, John Major developed Margaret Thatcher's theme of Britain as a share-owning and property-owning democracy.

Citing the spread of home ownership to more than two-thirds of UK households, Mr Major spoke of his vision of "wealth cascading through the generations", but the elderly and their middle-aged children are having to wake up to the fact that the family home may no longer be an inheritance, but rather an insurance against old age.

In the past, elderly people with chronic illnesses or an inability to manage on their own would be given long-stay beds in the NHS. Between 1988 and 1994, however, hospitals closed an estimated four in ten of their long-stay beds. Moreover, the government's Care in the Community policy allows only those diagnosed as needing specialist medical care to be kept in hospital. Simply being infirm and unable to manage is not enough.

Private nursing home fees are anything between £17,000 and £40,000 a year depending on the area and the intensity of nursing needed. If a local authority decides that an elderly person is not eligible for NHS care but should be cared for in a private nursing home, the person will be means-tested against the costs of that care. Under community care rules, elderly people with savings or capital of more than £8,000—and the value of their home is taken into account—will have to pay the full amount, while those with savings of between £3,000 and £8,000 will be asked to contribute to the cost of their care.

When the NHS was set up in 1948 it promised free care from the cradle to the grave. Now, a lifetime's tax and national insurance contributions are no guarantee of free care the nearer to the grave you get.

Source: Adapted from 'Care: the high price to be paid', *Observer,* 18 December, 1994 and 'It's that age-old problem', *Scotland on Sunday,* 25 June, 1995.

cern, however, that the new power to discharge patients might create difficulties and unpleasant media attention in certain situations, for example where elderly patients refused to leave and the hospital attempted to remove them forcibly. Critics also pointed out that locally determined eligibility criteria would produce inequalities in care provision between different areas of the country. In future, elderly people with similar conditions and circumstances may qualify for free NHS care in some places but not in others.

4 *Caring for the Carers?* In 1994 an OPCS survey suggested that 6.8 million people in Britain looked after elderly, sick or disabled people. 1.5 million of those had a full-time caring job. One in five was aged over 65. Eight out of 10 said they had no choice in taking over the caring role (the great bulk of care for the elderly and other dependent groups is provided by members of the family).

One of the main objectives of the community care legislation was to give a high priority to providing support for these carers. Although the importance of providing respite care has been recognised in a series of government policy documents, at the time of writing this had not been backed up by action. Carers still had no legal right to a social services assessment of their needs and nearly two years into the reforms, only 13 per cent of carers had received such an assessment. As a result, in 1994 only one carer in five received one week's break a year.

This inaction was occurring at a time when, in many ways, the position of carers was becoming more difficult. With the NHS offloading many of its responsibilities and with an increase in the number of early discharges from hospitals, many carers were having to cope with people who were even sicker than before. Surveys showed, however, that local authorities were six times more likely to help clients who were living alone than those living with carers.

It is possible, though, that demographic considerations may convince the government that it must take action to improve the lot of carers. Factors such as smaller families, the spread of divorce, the increased incidence of female employment and greater geographical mobility is likely to mean that the 'pool' of those willing to take on caring duties will decrease. This is something which the government would wish to minimise at all costs. After all, it has been estimated that if the services provided by these unpaid so-called 'informal carers' were paid for it would cost the public purse about £34 billion a year. If this 'free' support was seriously depleted, one of the major motives for the introduction of the community care reforms—to replace expensive nursing and residential care with cheap care at home—would be lost.

Community Care: The Future?

Changing demographic trends, rising expectations in the quality of health care and reductions in both the number of long-stay hospital beds and in the average length of hospital stay will mean that demands on community care services will almost certainly increase in the next decade or so. At the same time, it is likely that there will be fewer people available to take on the job of informal carers. Taken together, these developments will mean that questions such as how should community care be financed and what should be the boundaries between individual and collective responsibility will once again have to be addressed.

There are a number of possible options for the future funding and delivery of community care. One would be to ask the working population to pay higher taxes. This would allow the NHS and local authorities to retain their responsibility for long-term health and social care. Another would be to introduce a scheme of compulsory insurance against the risk of long-term care. This would be a move towards much greater individual responsibility.

The growing political power of the elderly will ensure that the one option which does not exist is to do nothing. For one thing, pensioners have significant consumer power. They also constitute one-quarter of the electorate (and due to demographic changes, this will increase in the coming years). Furthermore, a number of groups are emerging which are determined to flex the political muscle of elderly people.

Drawing lessons from the Netherlands, where pensioner political parties have won parliamentary seats, and from the USA, where the so-called 'grey lobby' is now regarded as one of the most powerful and influential political groupings, organisations such as the Pensioners' Liaison Forum and the Association of Retired Persons are hoping to harness the voting power of the elderly. Facing pressure such as this, all political parties will be keen to do something to allay the anxieties of older people about the costs and future direction of community care.

Chapter EIGHT
The Political Arena

IT IS OFTEN stated that health care is far too important an issue to be involved in politics. Since it is concerned with matters of life and death, so the argument goes, the only consideration in a civilised society should be how to achieve Aneurin Bevan's vision for the NHS of "universalising the best".

While such a view might have its attractions, it is difficult to see how political influences could ever be absent from this area. After all, the resources available for health care, and the way these resources are used, depend directly on political decisions. As we have seen, demand on any health care system is virtually limitless and governments will always have to make choices when allocating resources. This could be between various health care services or, indeed, between health care and other areas of government spending such as defence or education.

It becomes even more difficult if the distinction is drawn between 'Politics' (with a large 'P')—which refers to political parties and national and local government—and 'politics' (with a small 'p')—which refers to the way in which conflicts and disputes in everyday life are settled or changed. With this latter definition, it is clear that the NHS, like any institution, can be seen as a political world in its own right, with the balance of power being determined by whichever interest group can wield the most influence.

EMPLOYEES

The pay of health care employees is the main cost to the NHS—about two-thirds of its budget—and this inevitably gives these employees a significant opportunity to exercise influence. The sheer range of occupations and professions found within the NHS, however,—from consultants to catering staff, from senior administrators to trainee nurses—means that there are wide differences between the various groups of health care workers in their ability to influence decision making. Before looking in detail at the major groups, it is first of all worth considering the extent to which the composition of the NHS work force has changed in recent years.

Trends in the NHS work force

Table 8.1 shows how the number of NHS workers changed between 1981 and 1992. While there was a small decrease (nearly 32,000) in the overall number of NHS employees during this period, there were contradictory trends between the different sections of the work force.

The largest change in absolute numbers and in relative terms was in the number of ancillary workers. This was largely a result of the policy of competitive tendering (see Chapter 5), though many of these 'lost' staff continued to work within the NHS as employees of private contractors. It is also worth noting that there was a decrease in nursing staff during this period.

The biggest increase was in administrative and

Changes in NHS work force in the UK: 1981 & 1992

	1981	1992	Difference	% Change
Medical & Dental	49,700	58,800	+9,100	+18.3
Nursing & Midwifery	492,800	484,500	-8,300	-1.7
Professional & Technical	80,200	110,800	+30,600	+38.2
Administrative & Clerical	133,300	187,000	+53,700	+40.3
Ancillary	220,100	106,100	-114,000	-51.8
Other non-medical	56,200	53,400	-2,800	-5.0
Total	1,032,200	1,000,600		

Table 8.1
Source: Adapted from *Social Trends* 24, OPCS 1994. 7.40

clerical staff. This reflected a trend which had begun in the 1970s, although the *Griffiths Report on NHS Management* (see Chapter 3) and the *NHS and Community Care Act* of 1990 (see Chapter 4) provided the major impetus for this change. The professional and technical staff, which includes radiographers, speech therapists, occupational therapists and physiotherapists, also showed a substantial increase in numbers.

Doctors

Despite accounting for only about 5 per cent of directly employed staff, doctors are generally considered to have the most influence of all the interest groups involved in health care. Although almost all doctors work within the NHS, they have traditionally enjoyed a degree of independence which is quite unique among professionals employed by the state. The symbol of this privileged position was built into the NHS in 1948 and was based round the concept of clinical autonomy. Acceptance of this principle meant that doctors were given the freedom to use their own judgement to select who to treat and to decide what form the treatment should take.

Governments frequently consult with the profession through its representative groups and this has enabled doctors to influence health care policies. The British Medical Association (BMA), with a membership consisting of about three-quarters of practising doctors, is the most important of these groups. The BMA has campaigned on a wide range of public health issues—for example, alcohol abuse, smoking and boxing—and has used its network of parliamentary contacts to be able to claim credit for several pieces of legislation, including the compulsory wearing of seat belts. Most of its efforts, however, have been directed towards more sectional interests, such as doctors' pay and conditions of service, NHS funding and hospital closures. Although less prominent than the BMA, the Royal Colleges of Medicine are also often consulted by the government and this offers doctors another route through which they can influence health policy.

Neither the BMA nor the Royal Colleges, however, were consulted on the government's White Paper *Working for Patients* and the BMA's highly publicised campaigns against the reforms (see Chapter 4) may have been prompted as much by this exclusion as by the proposals themselves.

It would be wrong, however, to regard doctors as a single group, all with the same interests and the same ability to exercise power. Broadly speaking, doctors work in three separate environments: in hospitals, in general practice and in public health. Traditionally, there have been wide differences in status and influence both within and between these groups.

(a) Hospital consultants have always been regarded as the elite within the profession and they were virtually able to dictate their own terms on entering the NHS in 1948. Within hospitals, consultants specialising in the high-technology acute sector have been more successful in using their prestigious position to attract extra resources than have those working in the low status services such as mental health and the elderly. Junior doctors have the least influence, and the worst working conditions, of all doctors within hospitals.

The superior position of hospital doctors, especially consultants, has been threatened by recent reforms. The implementation of the *Griffiths Report* on general management in hospitals has reduced their influence, although not as much as the government had hoped. Of more significance was the introduction of market forces into the NHS and the setting up of Trust hospitals, since these developments have brought doctors to account in ways which would have been unthinkable in the past.

Despite this, hospital doctors still enjoy a privileged position and their ability to continue to win important concessions was underlined when, in 1995, the government, in the face of a threat of sanctions from hospital doctors, announced that they alone of all health staff would not be subject to local pay negotiations.

developments IN NURSING

1 Due to increasing concern about the exces-sive hours worked by junior doctors, along with management wanting to create a more flexible and cost-effective work force, nurses are being expected to take on tasks once seen as the domain of doctors. Duties now routinely carried out by nurses include taking blood samples, inserting drips and administering drugs.

Such changes provide opportunities for nurses to raise both their status and their ability to influence decision making.

2 As a result of the GP Contract, community nurses have had to take on extra responsibilities, such as running health promotion clinics, Well Women screening and immunisation and vaccination services. A pilot scheme set up in 1994 has allowed some community nurses to write prescriptions and it has even been suggested that practice nurses may be given the opportunity to become full partners with doctors in general practice.

Not all developments are positive however.

1 While the 1974 reorganisation had increased the involvement of nurses in management, the changes which followed the *Griffiths Report* of 1983 reduced their role at senior levels in the management structure. Although nurses could apply for general management posts, in practice few have been appointed.

2 The introduction of the internal market has forced managers of Trusts to examine the costs of providing care. Since wage bills for nurses form the largest expenditure of Trusts, fears have been expressed that one way in which managers may cut costs would be to put more nurses on short-term contracts and to employ a higher proportion of less qualified (and therefore cheaper) health care assistants in place of nurses.

(b) While having less political influence than hospital consultants, GPs have, nevertheless, successfully defended their position as independent contractors within the NHS. Indeed, the greater emphasis being placed on primary health care and the emergence of GP Fundholding in recent times seems likely to raise the status of GPs. It is possible that, in the future, it will be GPs rather than hospital consultants who will hold the dominant position.

(c) Public health doctors who work in the speciality of community medicine are by far the smallest of the three groups. They also have the least status and influence, although increasing awareness of new viruses and environmental health generally seems likely to improve their position.

Nurses

Nurses form by far the largest group of employees within the health service. There is a hierarchy within the nursing profession—ranging from chief nursing officer to first line nurse—and there are important differences between nurses who work in hospitals and those who work in the community as district nurses, health visitors and midwives. However, despite their numbers and their ability to command the sympathy of the general public, nurses have much less independence and political influence than doctors.

This can be explained, in part, by the fact that nursing remains a predominantly female occupation—approximately 90 per cent of nursing staff are women. Furthermore, a significant minority of nursing work is part-time—round 40 per cent of female nurses work part-time. In our society, jobs with these characteristics tend to be given low status and, of course, low wages.

Nurses have, moreover, traditionally suffered from an argument within their own ranks over strategy. On the one side were the Royal Colleges (the Royal College of Nursing and the Royal College of Midwives). Like the BMA, they tended to stress a professional approach. They concentrated on trying to improve the reputation of nurses by expressing concern for developing the appropriate skills and knowledge needed for the job and emphasising nursing's vocational role and loyalty to patients. On the other side were the trade unions, such as UNISON, which had a membership much wider than nurses to consider and which also regarded industrial action as a legitimate method for nurses to deal with their grievances.

The historic decision in 1995 by the two Royal Colleges to abandon their no-strike rules, though, may be an indication that the collective voice and political influence of nurses will be strengthened in the future. There have been other developments

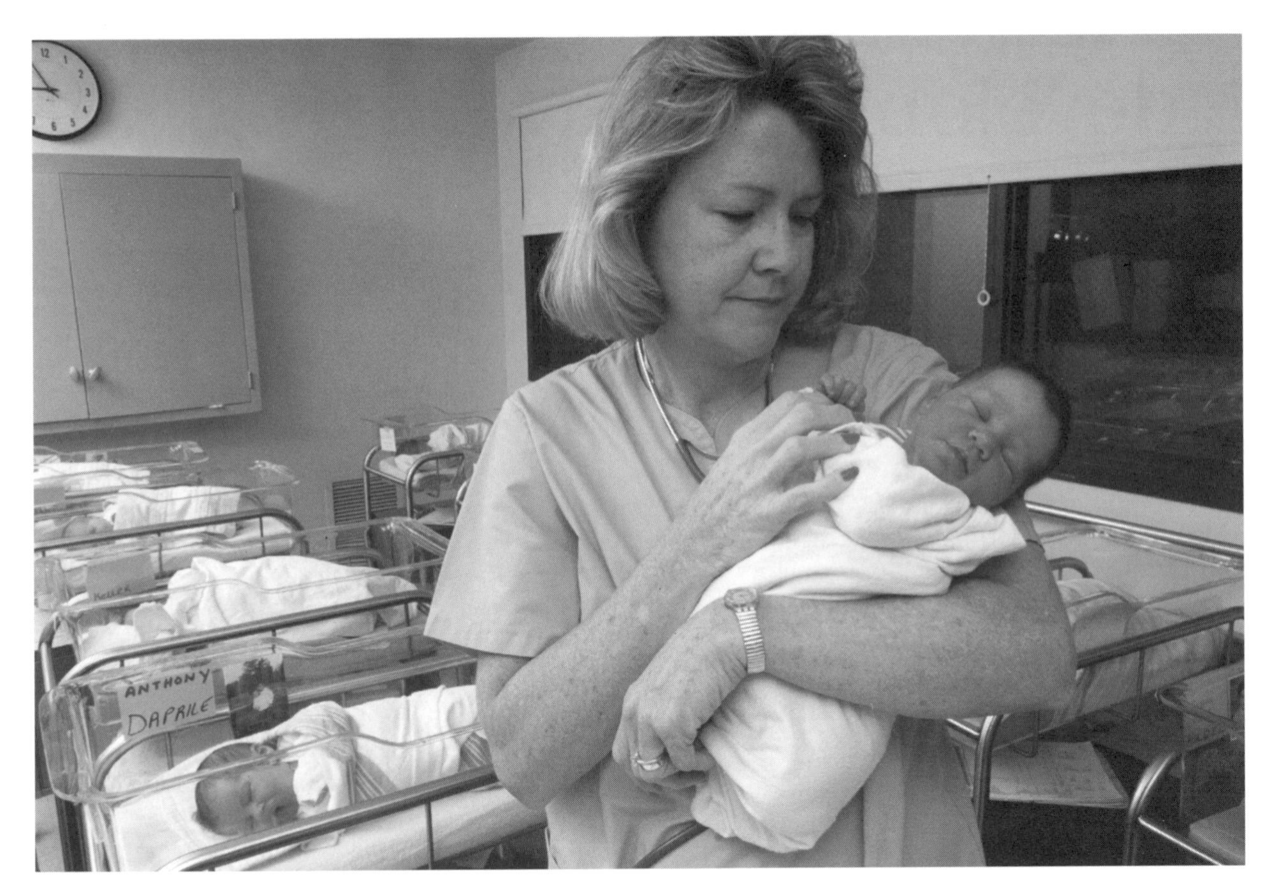

which have had an effect on the role and influence of nurses and these are explained in the box entitled 'Developments in Nursing'.

Managers

The 1982 reorganisation of the NHS emphasised decision making at the local level rather than by some central body. Consequently, health administrators found themselves more able to resist successfully the attempts of central government to implement national policies at the local level. It was always likely, however, that the centre would try to regain control over a system financed by the Exchequer. Indeed, the implementation of the *Griffiths Report* went some way to reimposing centralisation and, in so doing, reducing the influence of the administrators.

On the other hand, the 1983 changes also introduced general managers into the system and they were given, in theory at least, authority over all staff employed within their Region, District or Unit. The government's clear intention was that greater cost-efficiency and better use of resources would be achieved if general managers could effectively challenge the power of medical staff and, in particular, hospital consultants.

To what extent have general managers been able to exercise control over medical staff? The introduction of general managers had an immediate impact upon the nursing profession. As we have seen, nurses at senior level lost much of their influence in the management structure. In addition, the requirement on managers to obtain efficiency savings made many of them question whether some nursing activities could be undertaken by

cheaper unqualified staff. Managers found it easier than their predecessors to close hospital beds without having to go through lengthy consultations, but in most other areas managers continued to find it difficult to reduce the influence of doctors. The introduction of the purchaser-provider split in 1990, however, shifted the balance of power in favour of managers who could now use the threat of loss of contracts to pressurise hospital consultants into improving the efficiency and quality of their services.

Ancillary Staff

Ancillary staff carry out the low-status work within the NHS, such as catering, cleaning, laundry and portering jobs. Not surprisingly, perhaps, of all the service's employees they tend to have the least political influence. Unlike doctors, nurses and managers, they do not have the option of belonging to a professional body and have to rely on trade unions to represent their interests.

During the 1970s, there was an increase in both the level of unionisation among ancillary staff and in their willingness to use industrial militancy to achieve their ends. This helped to produce results and the average earnings of ancillary workers increased at a proportionately higher rate than doctors' earnings. Since 1979, the position of ancillary workers has been considerably weakened by the introduction of trade union legislation and, in particular, the move towards competitive tendering. Whether contracts have gone to in-house or private companies, the results have been the same, namely job losses, increased use of part-time staff and reductions in earnings and fringe benefits. Just as importantly, competitive tendering has weakened the power of the trade unions and, as a result, reduced the influence of ancillary workers still further.

VOICE OF THE PUBLIC

Members of the public, who pay for and use health care services, are another important interest group. There are various channels through which the public can exercise influence.

1 *'Consumerism'* and the principle of individual choice through the marketplace were encouraged by the various Conservative governments elected after 1979. It was hoped that if patients saw themselves as consumers they would be more willing to assert their authority over the activities of health professionals and, in so doing, help to improve the efficiency and quality of services. There were a number of initiatives aimed at promoting consumerism and consumer choice.

- Following the *Griffiths Report* on management, patient satisfaction surveys began to be used widely as a way of monitoring the views of patients. Most of these surveys concentrated on the quality of the hotel aspects of care, such as cleanliness, range of facilities and quality of food.

- The 1987 White Paper *Promoting Better Health* proposed that GPs should provide information about their services in a 'practice leaflet'. This White Paper also made it easier for patients to change their GP.

- The 1989 White Paper *Working for Patients* addressed a number of consumer issues such as the provision of more choice and the improvement of communications.

- The *Patients Charter* set out ten rights and nine service standards which patients could expect to receive.

The notion of consumerism, with its emphasis on customer relations, marketing techniques and performance targets has been criticised by some commentators as adopting a mere 'supermarket' approach. Of much greater importance, they have argued, are the concepts of representation and participation which enable the public to be involved in influencing decision making and policy.
2 *Community participation* has been achieved mainly through Local Health Councils in Scotland and Community Health Councils in England and Wales. These bodies were set up at the time of the 1974 NHS reorganisation and their role includes providing advice to people about the health service. They are also a means by which the public can voice their views on the NHS and influence policy making in health care at the local level. They are empowered to request information and can impose delays on the decision making process, although if they adopt too political a stance they can leave themselves open to the possibility of administrative reprisals, such as a reduction in their powers. Their ability to influence policy directly has, as a result, been somewhat limited.

The reforms following *Working for Patients* weakened community participation still further. For example, in Scotland the Health Boards' role as representative bodies for local authority opinion was diminished. In addition, not only were most Trusts set up in the face of public opposition, but the Boards of Directors of these Trusts are not directly accountable to the public since they are appointed by the Secretary of State. Finally, neither patients nor their representative bodies have the right to participate in contract planning. When looking at these developments, it is not difficult to see why some commentators drew attention to

LABOUR'S PRESCRIPTION FOR THE NHS

THE LABOUR Leader, Tony Blair, yesterday launched his Party's plans for the NHS. Labour has recognised the need to avoid a return to the inflexibility of the old NHS and promises to keep what is good from the Government's reforms and to remove what is bad. Mr Blair said that Labour's 38-page health policy document *Renewing the NHS* offered "a sensible third way to the future".

The document accepts many of the key elements in the Tory reforms—namely, the devolution of greater power and control and the separation of purchaser and provider responsibilities. On the other hand, it rejects the "market chaos" of the Tory NHS which it says has destroyed the national character of the service by creating a patchwork of competing businesses, shaking public faith in the NHS and reducing staff morale to an all-time low.

The main points of Labour's health plans:

- Purchaser-provider split to remain, but this will be used not to promote competition between hospitals but to ensure efficiency in the use of resources.
- Annual contracts to be replaced by longer term "health service agreements" based on cooperation between Health Boards/Authorities and hospitals rather than competition.
- Fundholding GPs to be phased out and replaced by alternative models of GP commissioning.
- GPs to be free to refer patients to any hospital.
- Hospital Trusts to be renamed "Local Health Services" and they will cease to control their own assets.
- Democracy in the NHS to be extended. Membership of Health Boards/Authorities and Hospital Boards to include more people from the communities they serve and Local Health Councils/Community Health Councils will have their powers strengthened.
- Compulsory competitive tendering for NHS support services to be abolished.
- Tobacco advertising to be banned.
- Tax relief on private medical insurance premiums for the elderly to be abolished.
- A Royal Commission to be set up to outline future options on the funding and provision of long-term care.

Source: Adapted from *The Independent* 'This prescription might do some good'(30 June 1995), and *The Guardian* 'Labour opts for compromise on NHS' (30 June 1995).

Liberal Democrats' Proposals to Improve the NHS

The Liberal Democrats' new policy paper *Build-ing On The Best Of The NHS* is a paper meant to put the patient first. Another organisational revolution would be catastrophic for staff morale and detrimental to patients. Liberal Democrats are determined to take the Tory reforms, shed the worst, keep the best and make them work.

We propose to retain the purchaser-provider divide to ensure that the NHS does not return to financial unaccountability. But competition based on price only will be replaced with competition founded on the quality and value of services.

We will lengthen the contracting cycle to ensure continuity and realistic planning. Trusts will not be able to gag their staff, and we will ensure they are more representative of local people. We will end the two-tier service by allocating a common basis of funds to GPs, whether or not they are Fundholders.

We will continue to fund centrally all health care needs, restoring free preventative dental and eye checks and freezing prescription charges. We know we cannot throw money into the system. We have proposed earmarking increases in tobacco tax for the NHS, significantly boosting funding.

Critics may dismiss it as a gimmick and yet just a 20p increase on 20 cigarettes would pay for our free preventative checks.

The higher the tax, the fewer the smokers, the less the NHS has to pick up the pieces of smokers' shortened lives.

Source: Adapted from *The Guardian Society* – 'NHS must take the middle way' (13 September 1995), by Alex Carlile, Liberal Democrat Health Spokesperson.

the contrasts in the government's attitude towards the public's ability to exert influence. While on the one hand, the government supported and encouraged consumerism, on the other, it opposed and discouraged representation and participation.

3 *Voluntary organisations* concerned with matters relating to health have rapidly increased in number in recent years. The principal concern of many of these organisations, such as Alcoholics Anonymous or the Down's Children's Association, is to offer support and advice to sufferers and their families, with less energy being directed towards influencing health care policy making. Others, though, such as Age Concern and the National Association for Mental Health (MIND), see their role quite clearly as pressure groups and aim to participate in the development of health policies. They attempt to gain publicity for their particular cause by exerting pressure through the mass media and by lobbying parliament. While they can point to several successes, they cannot threaten sanctions in the same way as doctors and nurses, or even ancillary workers, and their cooperation once policy has been implemented is not so vital. Consequently, their ability to exert influence is often relatively weak.

COMMERCIAL INTERESTS

The influence of industrial and commercial companies is another area which has implications for the formation of health policy.

1 *The providers of private health care services,* such as the private hospital groups and private health insurance companies, expanded their business significantly during the period of the Thatcher governments. As we saw in Chapter 5, the private sector was not able to achieve all it had desired from the government's reforms and, compared to other countries, it remains a relatively small part of the total UK health care sector. Nevertheless, it has had a considerable impact on the changing of attitudes and on the development of the idea that market forces should have an important role to play in the delivery of health care services.

2 *The drug industry* has managed to establish a fairly cosy relationship with the medical profession. The trans-national drug companies, such as Hoffmann-La Roche, provide most practising doctors with much or all of their postgraduate education, sponsor their academic conferences and fund their research programmes. This is not intended as a generous gesture: the purpose behind it is to encourage sales of their products. The fact that by 1991 doctors were writing out over 460 million prescriptions a year (or 8.1 per head of the population) suggests that this relationship with the medical profession is highly lucrative for the drug companies. The industry has, however, found it more difficult to dictate the development of health care policy and, as we saw in Chapter 3, the government acted against the interests of the pharmaceutical companies with its decision to substitute generic (unbranded) drugs for the more expensive brand name products.

3 *The alcohol, food and tobacco industries* employ large numbers of people, the sale of alcohol and tobacco provides the Exchequer with a great deal of tax revenue, and they present a healthy surplus on the balance of payments. During the last 30 years or so, however, there has been

an enormous amount of independent scientific research which has concluded that many people in the UK are unhealthy due to the fact that they drink too much alcohol, smoke too many cigarettes and eat the wrong kinds of food. The companies in these industries have countered by spending vast amounts of money on advertising their products and by lobbying doctors, journalists and politicians. The government has imposed some restrictions on the activities of these industries. There are advertising controls on alcohol and tobacco and the contents of food products must be clearly displayed on the label. Some critics, however, have argued that the government, for economic reasons, has taken a less forceful stance on regulating their activities than has been the case in many other countries. This, they say, illustrates the power and influence of these industries when they can help to shape health policy.

POLITICAL PARTIES

Health service employees, consumer groups and business corporations all lobby the political parties. The reason is that, depending on the results of the next general election, one of the political parties will be in a position to put into action policies which will support, or thwart, the interests of these groups.Considering the extent of this political activity, and the amount of public money devoted to the health care system, it is hardly surprising that health is generally regarded as one of *the* key issues in a general election campaign. Given the emotive nature of the subject and the possible political risks, however, politicians often seem more interested in 'point-scoring' against their opponents than in leading the electorate in an informed debate on health care.

In the lead-up to the 1992 general election, for example, all the major political parties included in their manifestos alternative policies on health care, particularly with regard to funding and the future direction of the outgoing government's reforms. While the Conservatives emphasised the increased funding which it said had been made available to the NHS since 1979, both Labour and the Liberal Democrats claimed that the NHS had been seriously underfunded. As could be expected, the Conservative manifesto sang the praises of their reforms and promised more Trust hospitals and more GP Fundholders. On the other hand, while both opposition parties accepted the division between purchasers and providers, they also stated their intention of getting rid of the 'internal market'. During the campaign itself, however, the debate hardly got beyond what the media called "the war of Jennifer's ear", which was a controversy over who had identified a young girl who had to wait for treatment for glue ear and who had featured in a Labour Party Political broadcast.

The health battleground for the next general election is now being drawn up. Both Labour and the Liberal Democrats have published policy papers on health (see newspaper articles on pages 86 and 87), so already it seems absolutely certain that health issues will remain at the very centre of the political agenda.

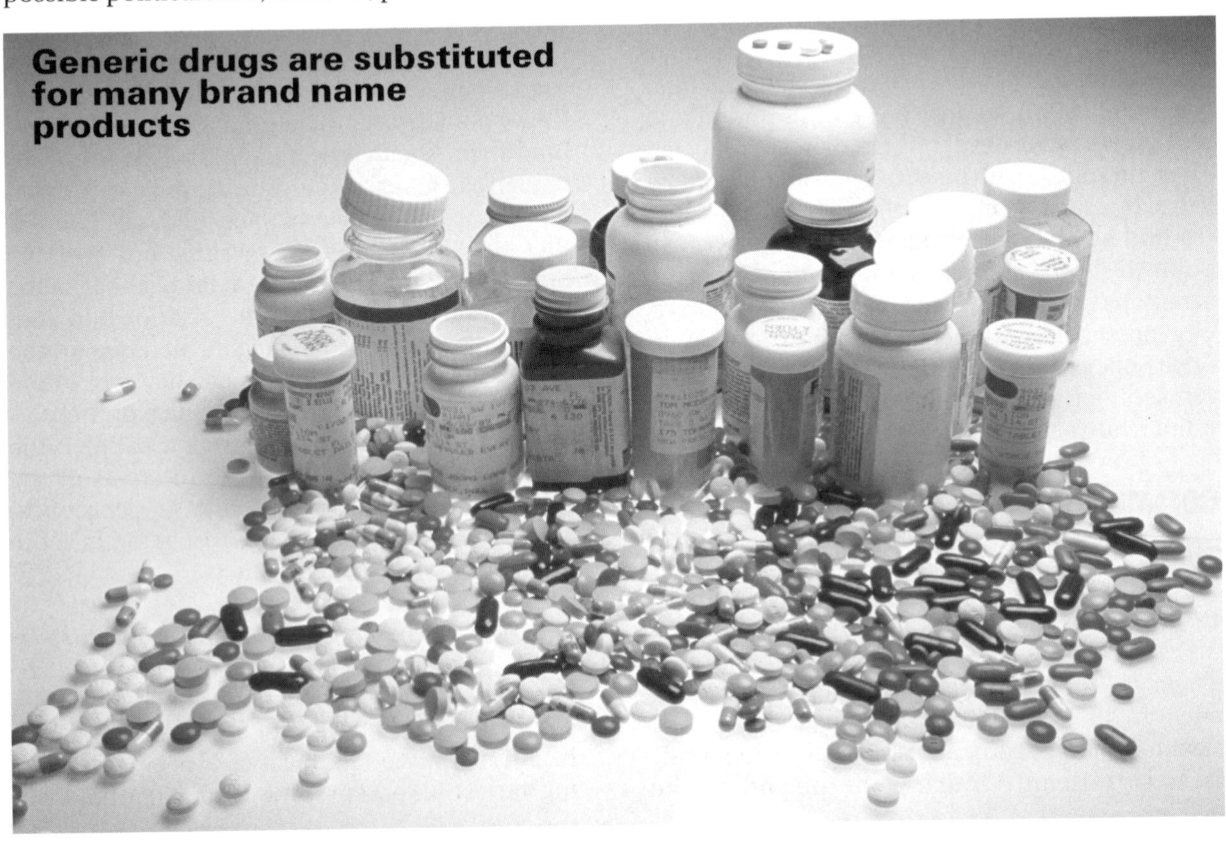
Generic drugs are substituted for many brand name products

Chapter NINE

Back to the Future

THERE ARE certain years which can be regarded as watersheds in the history of the politics of health care in the UK. These include 1948, the time of the creation of the NHS, 1974, the Service's first major reconstruction and 1979, with the report of the Royal Commission on the NHS and the election of a Conservative government committed to the principles of the market and individual responsibility. 1990 appears to have equally good grounds for being considered as another of these periods. After all, in June of that year the NHS and Community Care Act introduced the most radical shake-up to the organisation and delivery of services in the NHS's history, while in November the resignation of the Prime Minister officially brought the so-called 'Thatcher Revolution' to an end.

Writing five years after these momentus events of 1990 allows us to take a broad view of them and evaluate the impact they have had on the NHS. It is also an appropriate time to reflect on the achievements of the NHS and to examine some of the possible issues and directions of policy which may confront health care in the late 1990s and into the next century.

AN ASSESSMENT OF THE NHS

How successful has the NHS been? A clear enough question perhaps, but one which is difficult to answer. The problem centres on what criteria should be used to measure its achievements. An obvious starting point might be to examine the NHS's record in terms of whether it has been able to satisfy the original assumptions and aims dreamed up by its creators.

Fixed Quantity of Illness?

Beveridge had argued in his report that there was a fixed quantity of illness in society and that the setting up of a national health service would enable the backlog of demand to be met. Once that had been achieved, there would be a gradual reduction in the incidence of ill health and the number of cases the NHS would have to treat would eventually stabilise at a much lower level.

The reality, however, has been very different. Every measure of how much services are being used—whether it be the number of people turning up at GPs' surgeries, or the number of hospital treatments—points to the same conclusion. Rather than reducing to a lower level, the demands on the NHS have increased rapidly and consistently year after year.

With the benefit of hindsight, it is easy to see why Beveridge's assumption that there was a fixed quantity of illness was mistaken. The combined effects of medical progress and social change have meant that health problems have merely been transformed instead of being eliminated. Advances in medical treatment have greatly increased people's expectations of what medicine can do for them. People now expect treatment for conditions which in an earlier period would have been tolerated. While many infectious diseases have been largely brought under control, others have begun to replace them. The appearance of AIDS in the 1980s is a dramatic demonstration that the 'pool of illness' is never likely to diminish.

Improving Health?

A much more realistic hope was that a national health service would produce a greater improvement in the health of the British people than would have occurred had the previous ramshackle system (as described in Chapter 2) been allowed to continue. As we saw in Chapter 1, however,

A Balance Sheet

OF THE POPULATION'S HEALTH SINCE 1948

Good News

1 Infant mortality, generally regarded as the best indicator of a society's health status, has fallen dramatically since the NHS was set up. In 1948 there were 36 deaths for every 1,000 live births in the UK, but this had fallen to 6 deaths by 1993.

2 There have been significant improvements in the number of years we can expect to live. Life expectancy rose from 58 to 76 years for males and from 61 to 82 for females between 1948 and 1995.

3 Improvements in immunisation and antibiotics have meant that infectious diseases such as polio, diphtheria and whooping cough, which were major killers in 1948, have become clinical rarities today.

Bad News

1 There has been a significant rise in the incidence of chronic diseases, such as circulatory disease (heart disease and strokes) and cancers, in recent years. These diseases have been linked to modern lifestyle factors such as smoking, alcohol abuse, poor diet and lack of exercise.

2 As more people live into old age, the number of reported cases of physical and mental disabilities increases.

3 A number of 'new' diseases have attracted attention in recent years. The first case of AIDS (Acquired Immune Deficiency Syndrome) was reported in 1982, but by 1994 this had grown to 10,000, of which nearly 7,000 had died. Another disease which is causing concern is Creutzfeldt-Jacob disease, an infection of the brain transmitted in the diet, and which seems to be closely linked to a disease in cattle called BSE (Bovine Spongiform Encephalopathy).

while there have been many positive aspects of health experience in Britain since the creation of the NHS, there have also, unfortunately, been many negative aspects as well. A summary of these points can be seen in the box above.

Even with regard to the improvements, it would be a mistake to attribute all of them solely to the existence of the NHS. Improved nutrition, housing and education are, arguably, equally powerful factors which influence the health of the population. As the 1979 Royal Commission on the NHS admitted, how far improvements in health can be attributed to the NHS is "In one sense ... quite impossible to answer because there is no way of knowing what would have happened if the NHS had not been introduced in 1948." Furthermore, improvements in health care have occurred in all developed countries, irrespective of how they have organised their health services, and indeed in some of these countries the improvements have been more impressive than in the UK.

Collective Responsibility?

As was discussed in Chapter 2, the aim of Aneurin Bevan was to produce a national health system which was based on the principle of collective responsibility by the state. It could be said that this was achieved in 1948. After all, the very act of creating the NHS ensured that, collectively, the state assumed responsibility for providing a centrally organised system of health care.

Some critics have argued, however, that this principle has been steadily undermined since then. In particular, it has been claimed that the election, in 1979, of a Conservative government committed to increasing the powers of market forces and to encouraging the growth of the private sector, seriously threatened the notion that there should be a collective interest in the provision of health care.

On the other hand, some commentators have countered that the public's continuing support for the NHS limited the freedom of the government to achieve its real objective of a privately funded, insurance-based medical system. Whatever the reasons, Margaret Thatcher's government did not abandon its collective responsibilities and, indeed, it will go down in history as the first government since the service was created to spend more money on the NHS than on defence. Although John Major's government has shown itself to be equally committed to privatisation and free market economics in certain areas, for example British Rail, the Post Office and the Prison Service, it too has displayed little willingness to renounce the principle of collective responsibility for health.

Comprehensive and Free?

It is generally agreed that the NHS provides a wide (or comprehensive) range of services for the care and treatment of the population for most conditions. Indeed, improvements in medical technology and in facilities generally have meant that, in many respects, services have become even more comprehensive.

It is also the case, however, that some services have always received greater priority and a higher level of funding than others. In addition, long waiting lists have traditionally been used as a device to ration certain treatments. The decision to allow hospitals to 'opt out' gave rise to concerns that the comprehensive health service might be further eroded.

Some people have argued in favour of changing the basis of the way we pay for our health services by moving away from the present system, which is basically funded from general taxation, towards one based on private or social insurance with the opportunity for individuals to opt into a private insurance scheme. While there are arguments to be made for alternative funding systems—and, indeed, on two occasions Mrs Thatcher's governments seriously contemplated such a shift—taxation has remained as the principal source of funding. It is generally recognised that if tax funding was abandoned, the commitment to the principles of universality and comprehensiveness would be seriously compromised.

On the other hand, it can be claimed that the ideal of a 'free' service was conceded as early as 1951 when the Labour government introduced charges for dental work and spectacles. Successive governments have extended and increased these fees for NHS users (see Chapter 5). Nevertheless, some people have responded that, since charges for services have never contributed more than 5 per cent to the total NHS budget, the principle, in practice, has not been dispensed with, only modified.

Equal Access?

The aim of creating a uniform or equal standard of health care in terms of both quality and quantity for all citizens was always going to be a difficult objective to achieve. Part of the problem is that there are different interpretations of the term 'equal'. Equal can refer to an equal share of health care between individuals or between different groups of people or between different regions of the country.

With regard to one of these interpretations—the availability of services in different regions of the country—governments have achieved some success. There was, for example, an extremely uneven distribution of GPs around the country in 1948. Despite persistent inequalities *within* areas, particularly in London and other inner cities, the distribution of GPs *between* different areas of the country was significantly improved in the years following the establishment of the NHS. In other aspects, however, equality has been more elusive. As we saw in Chapter 6, people continue to have different ease of access to health care, different quality of health care available to them and different experiences of ill health. Despite the widely-held belief that we have a *national* health service, access to treatment varies according to factors such as where people live, their gender and to which ethnic group or social class they belong. Further, the so-called 'Cinderella' services for the mentally ill, those with learning difficulties and the elderly have always been under-resourced in comparison to the acute sector of care (this was dealt with in Chapter 7).

Indeed, it has been argued that the principle of equality of access has been weakened rather than strengthened in recent years. Among the issues which have caused concern have been the growth of the private sector (see Chapter 5) and the setting up of the 'internal market', 'opted-out' hospitals and Fundholding GPs. These developments have led to allegations that a 'two-tier' system of care has been created which has allowed the more fortunate to 'queue jump'. More recently, however, questions of fairness have been raised by the decisions of some health authorities to ration certain treatments. If patients are treated differently according to where they live, the principle of equal treatment for those in equal need is seriously undermined.

Conclusion

In many ways, then, the record of the NHS is a mixed one. It remains a service which is essentially concerned with the treatment of diseases rather than with their causes. It has been unable to eradicate ill health or eliminate inequality. It is at least questionable whether it can even take the major credit for the general improvements which have taken place in the population's health since 1948.

On the other hand, in comparison to health care systems in other developed countries, the NHS has proved to be very efficient and cost-effective. In 1994 it absorbed 5.7 per cent of GNP compared with twice that figure in the United States. Perhaps its main contribution, however, has been the creation of a system which ensures the availability of services to alleviate suffering and which, essentially, still remains free at the point of use. It is this, more than anything else, which has enabled the NHS to retain the widespread support and affection of the British people.

THE FUTURE OF HEALTH CARE

Any attempt at predicting the future direction of health care policy or the development of medical

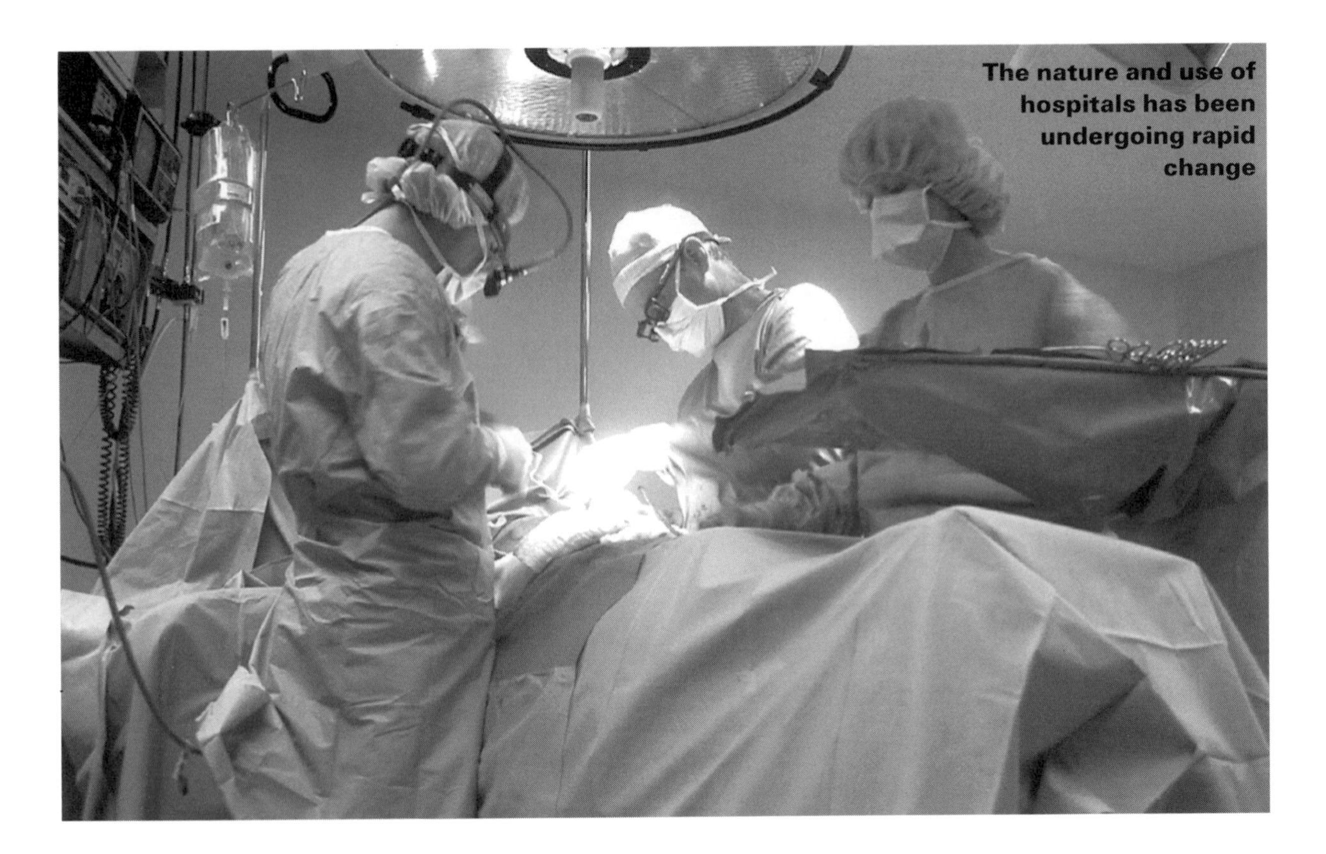
The nature and use of hospitals has been undergoing rapid change

trends is fraught with danger. For example, who, twenty years ago, could have prophesied the advent of AIDS. Or, indeed, as was discussed in Chapter 4, who would have thought at the time of the 1987 General Election that a no holds barred review of the NHS was just over the horizon?

We have to accept, then, that in any study such as this, there are likely to be more questions than answers. Despite this, certain trends and issues can be identified which seem likely to remain a feature of the health care debate throughout the next few years and into the twenty first century.

Changes in the Delivery of Health Care?

Throughout the history of the NHS, hospitals have been regarded as the most important element in the provision of health care. Their future dominant position in the system is, however, being threatened by a combination of political and economic pressures and technological developments.

Over the last few years, the nature and use of hospitals has been undergoing rapid change. While the number of acute hospital beds has been decreasing rapidly, there has, at the same time, been a steady rise in the number of cases being treated. This has been achieved by reducing the average lengths of time that patients stay in hospital and by increasing day surgery. What has made these developments possible has been advances in technology such as new drug treatments and the use of less invasive forms of surgery. It seems certain that government pressure on hospitals to reduce costs and find efficiency improvements will mean that the pace of these changes will accelerate in the coming years and that, as a result, there will be fewer available beds and hospitals will become smaller with many being forced to close down.

Another indication of the possible demise of hospitals has been the recent change in emphasis towards primary care, community-based services and preventive initiatives. Under the terms of their new contract, GPs have been encouraged to carry out minor surgery within their own practices, while some Fundholding GPs have suggested that they will consider opening on-site beds for their own patients' overnight stays. Elderly people, the largest single users of hospital beds, are increasingly being treated at home or in a GP-based unit. Recent technological developments, such as over-the-counter diagnostic kits, self-assessment through the use of personal computers and laser microsurgery at a GP's practice, will also mean that patients will have less need to attend hospitals in the future. While all the signs for a reduction in the number of hospitals are there to see, what is less certain is whether there will be the political will to implement these changes fully. After all, local hospitals remain popular with the public and, as we have seen, hospital consultants form a powerful interest group which is likely to offer strong resistance to hospital closures.

Funding Health Care?

One thing which can be said about the future of the NHS, with little fear of contradiction, is that

its expenditure will continue to rise. The proportion of GNP spent on the NHS is less than in most other industrialised countries but, in common with all of these health care systems, it is faced with the problems of an increasingly elderly population, the development of ever more expensive medical technology and almost limitless expectations. Since the price of medical services tends to rise faster than the rate of inflation, there seems to be an endless demand for more cash simply to maintain the existing level of services.

Although the NHS's supporters have argued that the bulk of its finances should continue to come out of general taxation—National Insurance contributions and charges make up less than 20 per cent of the total budget—this system does pose a problem. It means that how much the NHS is allowed to spend is largely determined by the state of the economy.

This has led some people to argue that additional financing should be introduced to top up money from the general taxation system. This was, for example, the conclusion of an inquiry *Healthcare 2000* which, in its report published in 1995, put forward the case for a number of possible options. These included a system whereby portions of tax would be specifically earmarked for the health service, and the introduction of charges for extra services within the NHS, such as private hotel-style hospital rooms, better food, treatments 'not universally provided' or for a place at the top of the waiting list.
It is impossible to say how this debate will develop in the future, but it seems certain that governments, whichever party is in power, will always be concerned with the costs of health care and with trying to promote efficiency and value for money. In the pursuit of these objectives, both politicians and those who work within the health service will be confronted with some very difficult decisions.

Rationing Health Care?

Another suggestion from the *Healthcare 2000* inquiry was that rationing of health services should be openly considered as a way for the NHS to save money. Officially, the government has refused to acknowledge that rationing exists in the NHS, preferring instead to use the euphemism 'setting priorities'. The essential meaning behind this term, however, is that some patients will not get treatment due to insufficient resources.

The truth of the matter is that there has always been rationing within the NHS. Traditionally, it has taken place implicitly, through devices such as queues, waiting lists and waiting times. Choices have always been made about which patients should receive treatment and which should not, although in the past doctors took these decisions in private. Doctors might have taken a patient or his or her relatives into a side-room and explained that all that could reasonably be done had been done. Cost might have been a factor behind that conclusion, but it would only have been the clinical decision which would have been mentioned.

Rationing came into the open, however, with the creation of the internal market. Contracts between 'purchasers' and 'providers' make clear exactly what services are being paid for and what are not. Purchasers now have to make explicit plans for the type and quantity of services they wish to buy within the limitations of their budgets. This was highlighted when Berkshire Health Commission announced that it intended to make £7 million of savings from its 1996/97 budget by issuing a list of 'low priority' operations (for example sex-change treatment and removal of wisdom teeth) for which it would no longer pay. The controversial issue of rationing was catapulted into the headlines, when, in 1995, a ten-year-old girl was refused treatment for leukaemia by Cambridgeshire Health Authority because they deemed that the £75,000 it would have cost to treat her would not have been an effective use of their rather limited resources.

Although rationing has become more open, many people continue to feel uneasy with the process due to the fact that decisions are being taken on an ad hoc basis by individual health authorities. Critics have pointed out that if the service is to remain a *national* one, it is unacceptable that treatments are available in one area but not in the next. They have argued that a fairer and more con-

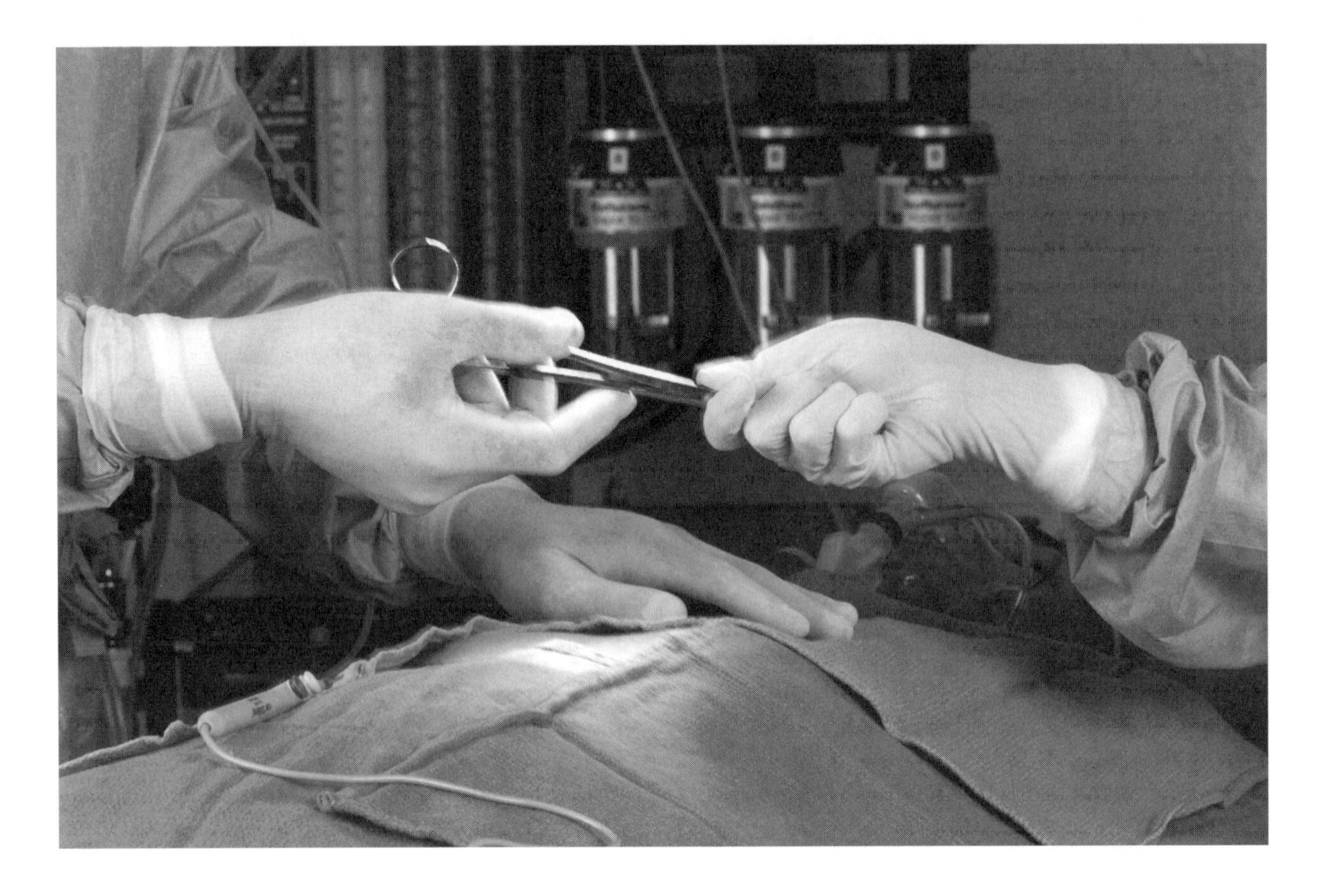

sistent policy must be developed and that this can only be achieved through politicians, in consultation with others, giving a much clearer lead from the centre by laying down guidelines and criteria regarding priorities and perhaps cut-off points for NHS treatment. Whether the politicians will be prepared to accept this responsibility, and the controversies which would undoubtedly accompany decisions such as why some clinical interventions should be available and others should not, is quite another matter.

QUALITY-ADJUSTED LIFE YEARS (QUALYS)

A technical approach to priority setting, and one favoured by many health economists, is to compute the cost effectiveness of treatment in terms of 'quality-adjusted life years', or QUALYs for short.

QUALYs are designed to take account of three different factors: the quality of life, the duration of life after treatment, and the cost of the treatment. QUALYs involve the consideration of a complex set of data, but the following simplified example outlines the basic idea behind it. Imagine two patients visiting a hospital for a consultation. One of them is in need of cancer treatment, the other a heart transplant operation.

The cancer patient, it is estimated, should be able to expect 10 years of life after the treatment. The patient will, however, have to visit the hospital frequently and may not be able to work. He or she cannot, therefore, be given a top quality of life score (which is 1) and, instead, is assigned a score of 0.7 for each of the 10 years, ie. 10 x 0.7 = 7 QUALYs.

The heart transplant patient is also expected to live for 10 years after the operation. It is believed that the operation will eliminate the patient's distress and disability altogether. The patient is, therefore, given the top quality of life score of 1 for each of the 10 years, ie. 10 x 1 = 10 QUALYs.

So far the heart transplant patient is doing better. It is at this point, however, that the cost of treatment is taken into consideration. Suppose the cancer treatment costs £25,000, while the heart transplant operation costs £50,000. This would mean that two cancer patients could be treated for the same price as one heart transplant patient. In other words, for £50,000 each cancer patient would receive 7 QUALYs, which for the two patients amounts to a total of 14 QUALYs. On this basis, then, cancer treatment now emerges as better value for money than heart transplant treatment, and so it would be the cancer patient who would be given priority.

The great attraction of QUALYs is that it carries out the assessment of patients' needs by a method which is explicit, consistent and fair. The concept, however, also has its critics. Doubts have been expressed over the methods used to collect the data and the accuracy of the conclusions being drawn from it. Who should set the values on different states of health? What criteria should be used? Should a person's contribution to society, for example employment status, age and mental ability, be taken into consideration? Will a distinction be made between treatments which are life-saving and those which are not? Others have argued that what the NHS needs is more money, not a technical method to prioritise resources. If the principle of QUALYs is accepted then, it is claimed, the right to fight for more resources is conceded.

More Cost-Effective Health Care?

Some health economists have questioned the need for introducing alternative funding systems or methods of rationing services into the NHS. Instead, they have argued that a better starting point would be to examine ways of how the NHS could spend its money more wisely and how to make use of developments in science which are enabling the service to develop better and more cost-effective methods of treatment. In 1991 the Department of Health set up a Research and Development Unit and part of its remit was to examine the evidence of clinical trials to find out which treatments actually work and which do not. It has been estimated, for example, that anything between £100–£200 million is being wasted every year on unecessary gynaecological operations such as hysterectomies. Furthermore, the Audit Commission has calculated that £420 million a year could be saved by stopping inappropriate drug prescribing by GPs and that unnecessary X-rays cost the NHS another £20 million a year.

One of the great successes of the NHS is the number of operations and treatments which it now can offer patients and which in 1948 were unheard of. This creates a difficulty for the NHS, however, since new treatments increase demand and therefore add to costs. Now, though, there are some new innovations which promise to save the NHS money. For instance, more than 45,000 hip replacements are carried out in Britain every year. The problem with artificial hip joints is that they do not last forever and nearly one in five have to be replaced. An artificial bone which encourages real bone to grow into the implant surface is being developed and when it comes into use it is estimated that it will save the NHS around £80 million every year. As a result of such developments, it is claimed that the view that the NHS will require either billions of extra pounds or have to look at ways of introducing further rationing simply to keep the same level of services, is a mere myth.

Conclusion

There remain many other uncertainties about the future direction of health and health care policies. For example, how will the relationship between the private sector and the NHS evolve? Will interventionist measures be introduced to tackle the ever persistent social, geographical, gender and ethnic inequalities in health? What can be done to resolve the problems which have arisen from the community care arrangements and, in particular, the boundary disputes between what is regarded as 'health' and 'social' care?

One of the biggest uncertainties, of course, is knowing what the outcome of the next general election will be. As we saw in Chapter 8, while there appears to be a wide measure of agreement between the major parties on the desirability of maintaining and protecting the basic principles and goals of the NHS, there are important differences with regard to how best to achieve them. If Labour wins the next election, for example, it seems likely that Trusts and Fundholding GP practices will be phased out and that 'competition' within an 'internal market' will no longer have a place in the system.

There are some things which can be said with a fair degree of certainty, however. Health matters will, as always, feature as a key issue in the next general election campaign. Whatever directions the public and private sectors take in the future, or what solutions and medical breakthroughs are found, there is no doubt that it will all be done in the context of the politics of health care and that it will stimulate a great deal of debate.